THE
THREE FOUNTAINS

THE
THREE FOUNTAINS

BY

STARK YOUNG
AUTHOR OF "THE FLOWER IN DRAMA"

NEW YORK
CHARLES SCRIBNER'S SONS
1924

CONTENTS

THE
THREE FOUNTAINS

THE THREE FOUNTAINS

I

VITALITY IN ART

WE decided to stop for the night at Partinico instead of Castellamare and go on to Segesta next day. Castellamare is the usual place for tourists, and Baedeker was distinctly silent about hotels elsewhere. Partinico, according to him, was a town of twenty-three thousand six hundred and sixty-eight inhabitants and a centre for the wine trade; it lay "⅔ M. to the left of the station" and was "defended by several old towers," and that was all.

But, I argued with myself, if it is a wine centre, there must be places where the buyers stay. Guide-books took a pampered view of hotels. Very likely the hotels of Partinico lacked formal gardens and central heating. But if the Italians could stand it we could. Why be stale?

We took the white road up the hill to the town. The beautiful country people passed by,

going home after the day's work, with their
donkeys and hayforks and scythes. Some of
them were singing. And the white road along
the gray-green country, the clear stream, the
oleanders and vines and olive-trees, the still sky
after twilight, the light reflected from the
ground, and the first pale stars coming out, the
people with their goats and asses and sheep, and
the rose and white and yellow farm houses where
the dogs were barking — all this gentle, clear
world went together; it was perfect, it was all
Theocritus over again. Theocritus, the warm
and gentle poetry of it, its quiet vividness and
animation and pathos.

At the edge of the town the smell of wine
arose, a sweet, fermenting, heavy fragrance, the
famous Partinico. The air of the town was like
one long *al fresco* tavern. And when we came
into it, the hum of the piazza was just dying
down, the bright voices were trailing off home.
Darkness had come suddenly, and infinite stars.

We looked about us. The Stella was on the
piazza, the *capostazione* had told us. But we
saw no name, no entrance. I asked a young
man. The hotel—ah, rather! he said courteously;
the signori would find the hotel just there, on

the left. He pointed out the indistinguishable Stella with one of those precise, convincing gestures that a South Italian would use to point out the end of the world if you asked him its direction. That finger of his spoke to the very muscles within us, and we followed it as one always does when these people direct, one's body moving forward as if by a natural law before they have done speaking.

We took the street the young man pointed out and walked along. It was much darker once you left the piazza. We walked three blocks but saw nothing of the Stella. We turned back and asked again. The hotel was now on our right, just off the piazza. We missed it again. Finally we asked a lean, dim man propped against a wall if he would take us to the door of the hotel. He bowed and turned to a low, arched doorway beside him and we followed him up a dark, winding stair. There were only smells and pitch darkness as we followed the sound of the man's footsteps.

We entered a big room with a pile of bedding to one side, a long table with chairs, and an old square piano in the corner. Our escort went for the *padrone*. We could already hear a man's

3

voice shouting and swearing and the clash of pans in the adjoining kitchen. A parrot sitting on the window-sill began to rap on the glass with his bill and shout, *"Chi è? Chi è?"* Who's there? Then our guide came back, followed by a brigand, tall, scowling, and gruff, the *Signor Padrone.*

There were no two rooms with one bed, the *padrone* said, and no one room with two beds. There was a one room with three beds but one of them was taken; a signor had the room already. We could have that if we liked. He did not smile all this time. By now my brain was already teeming with Sicilian horrors and I was wondering if we should ever get out of this place alive. The tariff for these, the *padrone* said, would be three lire a bed. Twelve cents, I thought, grotesquely; I might be murdered, but my bed was to cost me twelve cents, by exchange. I asked if there was any other hotel in Partinico. There was not; and we were shown to our apartment, where we left our kit and returned to the *salone.*

The *padrone* went out and cursed the kitchen people again and came back and sat down facing me. He inquired whether we were buyers

4

or what. His manner implied that we were probably what. I explained that we were travellers. I tried to be winning; I declaimed about Sicily; I said the war had been fought for nothing; that Italy had won her war and lost everything; that all there was to France was *egoismo*. These were the things I had heard harangued and agreed upon in the trains and hotels, and by the barbers, and by the stewards on the Palermo boat. The *padrone* softened a little but did not unbend.

"You are right, signore," he said; "Italy has won the war and lost everything. We are ruined. If there is another war we would not fight for France."

He rose and went to the kitchen. A moment later a sullen, ragged maid hurried in to set the table. Appalling guests were coming in: a man with a great black hat, a sooty face, and a kind of club or blackjack stuck through his belt; a small man with one eye, very fierce and quick; a giant with a silk bandanna around his neck, a huge mustache, and a peaked cap on the back of his head; and a younger and more inconsequent scatterbrain, at whom the others glared; he was plainly from a distance, as appeared presently

when he spoke of his business in Amalfi. But
after a little, as supper progressed, the maid, in
her tatters, seemed to cheer up. She began to
slap one of the guests in the face with her apron,
the merchant from Amalfi. The two were evidently on a footing, and I began to feel more
comfortable; much better a dinner of herbs where
love is, I thought; the prophet had said that,
and at such times one gladly believes in the
prophets. And after a time the *padrone* came
in and joined the conversation. He, too, seemed
gradually a little more human.

After supper we paid our bill and went out
to walk about the darkened main street of the
town under the incredible stars till eleven o'clock.
The idea was that our roommate should get to
bed first and we before we slept should see what
sort of creature he proved to be. We had an
ice, bought salami and cheese and bread for
to-morrow's lunch, and walked about the church
porch.

But when we returned our roommate had not
come in. We must go to bed and leave the door
into the passage open for him.

I put my money — thousands of lire that I had
just exchanged for a few hundred dollars — and

6

my watch into one of my shoes and blew out
the lamp. A lantern from the piazza fell through
the open window over the walls of the room, silver and faint like moonlight.

My friend, who was a Harvard philosopher
and, to top off his philosophic scorn of chance and
fate, knew nothing of the stories of Sicily and
lonely places, went off to sleep. We were to be
up at five and had ten miles' walking at Segesta;
but I had made up my mind to stay awake until
the other man came in.

I had said to my friend that I wished to be
present at my own murder, but I did not any
longer expect to be murdered exactly. I knew
now that I could yell out of the piazza window
and to the *padrone*, whom I now saw to be no
murderer, however much of a thief, a bully, and
a wife-beater he might dwindle into. But as I
lay on my pad on those wide boards beneath
me, I thought of the possibilities and the stories
I had read. Every one knows about that Sicilian
closet door showing the crack of light and beginning to slide open, and if the traveller had not
had his pistol — and so on. Every one knows
of the kidnappings for ransom, the robbing.
Every one knows of the man who was shut up

in an abandoned sulphur mine till his friends sent the money demanded. There is the Black Hand too. And neither Baedeker nor the government itself will insure safety in these remoter parts in the west of Sicily. I preferred at least to see who the man was that was to share our room.

I leaned down for my shoe and put it on the other side of the bed next the wall. Then I tried to remember that Samuel Butler had done a great deal of his writing not far away at Calatafimi; and that at Carini, a little to the east, Lais was born and stolen away to Greece in 415, when she was a girl of twelve. I tried to think of all the princes who might have come from afar to seek her favors, so great was Lais' renown in the world, and of the gifts they offered her, objects and ornaments such as one sees in the Naples museum or in Athens. I revived diligently the memory of those lion-handled cups that might have been brought and laid at her feet, those jasper amulets, and rings of chalcedony, and even Egyptian jewels wrought with such gravity and lordly style. I wondered if Lais dreamed ever in those great days of these rocks at home and the sea beneath Carini;

or if she remembered the twilight that I had seen that evening, so tender and ardent and still.

The clock in the piazza struck twelve. And soon after that some one began to play the piano in the dining-room at the end of our passage. The piano was like so many pianos in Italy; it trilled and banged with a tinkling, brassy loudness like a hurdy-gurdy. Then a lady began to sing *Una voce poco fa*, from *The Barber of Seville*. Her voice was a high soprano, better than some on the opera stage, a little shrill at the top, very exuberant and fioritura and bright. She played and sang full style as if we had been at the Teatro Massimo in Palermo, "*Una voce poco fa* ——"

"Well," I thought, "at midnight, in a hotel, just outside the doors of the bedrooms! At the top of one's bent! This is astonishing."

The lady sang on; the clock struck one. Sometimes she played a waltz and rested her voice. Then she began again, trilling a great deal. She was tireless. But no one seemed to object, and there was not any other sound in the hotel save once when a guest came in and stopped for a moment to speak with the singer. At this

9

she sang for the third time, plainly by request, *Una voce poco fa.*

Just before two o'clock the door opened and the other man came in. I could not see his face in the dim light, but I could see that he was tall and wore a slouch hat.

"Good evening, signore," I said at once, rather too alertly perhaps.

"Signore, good evening," he said in a full voice, taking off his hat, and throwing it on the table. "You are not asleep?"

No, I was still awake.

He did not light the lamp but began undressing in the dusk of the room. I could see that he had taken off his shoes, his collar, and his trousers and then got into bed.

"You are getting in late to-night, signore," I said.

"On the contrary," he said. "Last night I was out until three."

But were there parties at Partinico at such an hour, I asked, or a carnival indoors, or what? I should not have thought — or was there a beautiful signorina?

No, he had been with friends. He was getting ready to take an examination. For what? He

10

was going into teaching; he was to have a position in a government school. I asked why he wanted to take up the teaching profession.

"But, signore," he said, "I have been an auctioneer. I have auctioned horses since I was fifteen. I prefer some work where I can use the mind better. I like books."

"But you must sleep late in the morning or you will be tired out and do badly on the examination, will you not?"

On the contrary again, he had come in later than this, much later, last night and had risen at seven.

"Listen, signore," he said suddenly, "excuse me."

The singer had begun a new aria. "It must be two o'clock," I thought. But the man went on as if he were in an opera box:

"Do you know what that is?"

"*Lucia*, isn't it?"

"Yes. You like it?"

"Yes, indeed. But tell me, signore, who is the singer?"

"The *padrone's* daughter," he said.

"The daughter of the host! A member of the establishment, so to speak, making so free

11

with the hours!" I thought, but I said only, "Ah — " He had risen and gone to the door.

"See what kind of voice she's got," he said, opening the door halfway and going back to bed. We could now hear every syllable.

"Good voice. Brava!" he said, as soon as he lay down. "Ah, — la, la — " he began to accompany the singer softly.

And then at the finale, he sat quickly up in bed and cried:

"Ah! There, signore, that's beautiful! Good!"

But the singing was over, and he lay down again; the piano, after a tremendous crescendo banging, stopped, and soon I could hear by his breathing that he was asleep.

By this time I did not care whether I slept or not. Nothing mattered, I was so excited with it all: the singing at this time of the night and nobody minding; the voice, the old arias, in this lonely town; the light in the room; and, most of all, the man who loved this music, who was leaving his auctioneer's business for a work with books, and who could come in after two o'clock and get up at seven for two nights running and take examinations. And the tirelessness of it

all, the love of beauty! The zest for life, the
inexhaustibility!

These people belong to the sun, I thought.
The sun brings up the life in them as it does in
the grapes, the flowers, the abundant world
around them. No wonder their gods and saints
and the forms of life and death and beauty that
they have built are clear and beautiful. No
wonder the tragic quality they have goes, not
with dimness and mystery and Gothic confusion,
but with clear outlines, violet mountains, and
myrtles, the white rocks, and the blue sea. Their
art can well afford restraint and graciousness
when there is such a flood of vitality welling up
for it. Getting up to open the door at half
past two o'clock to see what kind of voice she
has!

When we stole quietly out of our room at five
next morning, we found the *padrone* sitting by
the long table, wrapped in a shawl and smiling
as he gave us a pleasant journey.

But later on, as the train rattled along to
Segesta, I asked myself wofully: What chance
have we got compared with these people? I
thought of the story of how Rossini writing in
bed one winter morning dropped his manuscript

of an overture on the floor and how, rather than crawl out of bed after it, he wrote another one. I thought of Lope de Vega pouring out plays by hundreds; of Leonardo with his painting, his sculpture, chemistry, botany, and geology; his designs for steam propellers, flying machines, jellies; the sketches for fortifications, bridges, and wedding-cakes he made for the Sforzas; and the profound and beautiful notes he kept for himself. I thought of a soprano in Madrid in a difficult little opéra bouffe, singing twice and sometimes four times a day, in her two-hundredth performance when I heard her, and fresh as a bird. The sun outside flooded the violet mountains and the lemon-colored rocks. I saw a stream-bed filled with wild irises. On the side of a hill I saw a black grove of pines, a thin line of smoke rising above it. A hard, finite, infinite, subtle world. Then I thought of our Northern nerves, our exhaustions; of Fellows' Hypophosphites; of my friend who goes up to Peterborough to get enough vitality to finish a one-act play.

II

GOOD FRIDAY AND CLASSICAL
PROFESSORS

I ARRIVED at Girgenti early in the morning of
Good Friday and went straight from the hotel
to the cathedral for the ceremonies.

All Girgenti is tawny-colored and dull rose
and white. It is a stern, dry city, lying on the
sunbaked hill like a lion. The streets are steep
and winding in every direction, deep as caverns
and full of stairs. Rising up in these streets
are the church fronts, full of Spanish and Arabic
memories, rich, baroque, heavy, barbaric, half
cruel, like so much of the town. Many of the
streets look down on the sea below. And at
night through the columns of the temples outside the walls I have seen the sea shining in the
starlight.

This city was the Acragas of the Greeks, the
Agrigentum of the Romans, and has been Car-
thaginian, Saracen, Spanish, as well as Italian.
All that is left of its larger glories is the cathedral,
for the temples lie now in the country. The

15

cathedral is a huge thing on twenty feet of stairs, faded golden stone, honey-colored in the light, and falling away here and there into ruin. The vast doorway opens into an interior still more ruined. Enormous columns lead up to the broken vaulting and make an aisle between the high altar of the choir at one end and at the other to the great crucifix with the life-sized figure of Christ. In many places under foot the pavement has come away and the bare earth appears.

There was a throng of people, standing praying, talking, quietly watching each other, and looking on at the mass. From behind a column somewhere an organ was playing. Clouds of incense hung about, and there was a smell of spring flowers. A procession of priests, acolytes, seminarians, and choir-boys came from the sacristy and moved slowly to the choir, toward which ran a long strip of brocade leading to the altar itself. Two of the priests in the procession came up before the steps, putting their palms together in front of them, and knelt down on their knees and kissed the earth. Then another two of them came, knelt down and kissed the earth. And so on, all the procession, two by two, slowly, all kneeling to kiss the earth before

16

they went up the steps. A bell rang and the
people dropped to their knees. Meanwhile far
down in the cathedral you could hear the organ
playing; and in the choir, where the candles
burned against the dim stone and faint mist of
old frescoes and old blackened canvases of saints,
the priests chanted.

That night before midnight I was awakened
by a music of trumpets and cornets and pipes,
a dirge, in a strange mode something like the
music I had heard once among the Arabs. I
went to the balcony and saw in the deep and
narrow streets below, against the tawny stone
and wild heavy shadows, a procession of people
streaming past. They carried, every one, some
sort of light—lanterns made of paper on staffs,
and candles and torches; and they chanted as
they marched. Their lights were not carried
overhead or on the shoulders, as our processions
do, but down at the waist; and so made a marvellous effect; they did not make a mere glitter of
lights and sparks above darkened figures, but a
throng of glowing shapes, lighted forms and
faces, in the darkness, moving along and casting
incredible shadows on the steep walls and houses.

At the head of the procession they had carried

17

past the Virgin, wreathed with flowers and standing on a kind of platform surrounded by lamps; the stiff image under its velvet canopy contrasted strangely with the human forms moving below. Afterward there were people for a long time making the procession, and presently they brought the figure of the dead Christ, taken down from the crucifix in the cathedral and laid on a bier in a glass coffin, with lamps burning around Him, moving slowly, with the dirge playing and the people chanting it: the pallid figure with its bleeding side and its crown of thorns, and the strange hypnotism again of the still form above the motion of the figures below. Then the endless procession again, filing past, with more music, the lighted bodies in the old streets, their shadows, the dirge playing on the horns, in the darkness.

I stood on the balcony long after the last of the people were gone and the music had died away in the far-off streets. The stars were shining; they were near the earth and golden-colored. It was all beautiful and strange and pagan; it was barbaric, ancient. It had the sense in it of passionate continuity, of the unbroken relation to the old life of the earth, to the soil, to light,

to motion and things. It brought to my mind
the memory of those early dark races, half unknown to history, whose strains made a part of
the ancient blood and spoke in the shadowy
omens and cults and secret rites. Demeter,
the Earth Mother, wandering in search of her
child; Mary, the Mother of God, going to find
her son; the strange music on the horns, the
torches, the mourning for Adonis, the dead god
carried on the shoulders of his mourners, the
flowers, the old city, and the spring night — the
life of the Mediterranean, ancient, continuous,
unbroken! Moments like this have in them the
quality of the life of men and the life of the
earth become one; the body becomes one with
the things of the world; the uplifted hand lifts
up the heart with it; the lanterns and shadows
are not only in the street, but shine and darken
in the soul.

From all this strange, wild beauty and poetry
I subsided next morning with coffee and rolls
to thoughts of our professors of the classics.

Classical professors! I thought of their plaster
casts, white as chalk and dry as ashes; of their
dens and studies full of weak water-colors of
Roman ruins, and spotted with photographs and

brown prints of the Parthenon and Apollo's head
and the Forum and a litter of pigmy reproduc-
tions from Pompeii. I thought of their Cicero-
nian jargon and Roman platitudes. They have
done well, no doubt, with maxims suited to the
making of men and to the building of empire.
They can lash the new time with their bull-
headed old Cato and his pristine virtues — how
much better they inculcate Roman middle-class
morals than Greek light. I thought of Æschylus
in majestical sleepy imitations of Shakespeare;
and of Euripides filled with a sighing Tenny-
sonian bliss and languishments of lovely lyricism
that would make a Greek stampede; and of
Plato draped in the solemnities of the Christian
language.

I sat on and on there at my balcony table in
Girgenti that morning with my coffee, which
was very bad, looking down into the daylight
street where the procession had passed the night
before. I was thinking now of those classical
exhibitions I had seen in seminaries at home,
the young ladies going through soft Delsarte
movements, wrapped in cotton as it were, in
their cheesecloth dresses, white with white fillets
and Psyche knots, and girdles crossing over their

breasts; posturing with their lovely arms and looking through white hoops, very nice and proper surely and nothing demonstrative about them. Delicate academic shadows they were, nymphs of our safe classic groves. The picture came to me of the professor reading Martin's translation of Catullus to the college class. We came to the Lesbia poem:

> soles occidere et redire possunt:
> nobis, cum semel occidit brevis lux,
> nox est perpetua una dormienda.

I heard the pitiful necessity of that gerundive in *dormienda,* and the cadence of it, the poetry of lament, full of incantation and despair; and then I listened while the professor gave us Martin's rendering:

> Suns go down but 'tis to rise
> Brighter in the morning skies;
> But, when sets our little light,
> We must sleep in endless night.

And with that, somehow, I thought of that dirge in the harsh stone city and then of Dante, mediæval but the son of the ancient passionate art; and then of the dulness and gray wash of

21

Professor Norton's translation, commended in schools. I thought of those modest exhortations and mottoes and those chaste renderings of ancient authors into English. I thought of those fig-leaf editions of the poets of Greece and Rome. Fig-leaf professors!

Alas, alas, alas! How much do they know of all this that I saw, with the kissing of the ground before the altar candles and the host in the tabernacle; the pale god and his mother, and the music and torches through the old streets? Do the professors really believe that the temples had yellow capitals or red columns with blue capitals and gilded acanthus leaves? Do their eyes remember that sometimes behind the rocks and oleanders you saw at the head of a valley a vermilion shrine? Why then the ashen casts? How far do these men, when they are sorting out of Plato and Hesiod the desired order and discretion, and making up, from these rich forms, their little almanacs of platitudes or their contributions — not to be despised, of course — to the mass of ethical and institutional thought and theory — how far do they conceive at all, alongside the social theory and ethics, those other forces working in the ancient minds:

beauty and madness, fierce changes, barbaric blood, sudden earthly poetry, and darkness; so much of which was here in Girgenti still, though all the wider intellectual aspects of the ancient life had dropped away from it?

Just what, I wondered, as I sat there in Girgenti, would many of these classical professors have thought of Acragas, Pindar's most beautiful city among mortals. For that matter, what sweeping judgments would they have passed on those ceremonies by night at Eleusis, those rites, those processions in the darkness, those orgies, which their admired Sophocles and Plato took so seriously! — how the early Christian fathers shuddered at them and shunned them and those nights as the devil's own, we know already. And if the professors should come suddenly from those studies of theirs and from those healthy, callow boys they teach, and should see this Good Friday at Girgenti, see something of the reality of the thing they have so innocently been professoring about, the human eternity of it, see so much of the old life and the passionate soul of the Mediterranean lasting on here, what would they think of it? The inauguration of the president of the college is not very interesting, to be sure, but then it has to be undergone, and, after all, one must join in it. But this matter of Girgenti and the ceremonies? One cannot help liking the Sicilians, of course; they are like children, and almost anything in these ancient lands is of interest to the classical student. It is all picturesque certainly, an odd piece of paganism, crude, unsanitary, or, at best, a suggestive bit of folk-lore and survival of tradition. Alas, nevertheless, I thought, what a limitation in me that when I had seen for myself so moving and complete a thing I should think of anything or any one besides! I was worse than the worst professor to be concerned so here in Girgenti over distant matters.

But steadily, in the midst of these ashen thoughts and driving them finally quite out of my mind, the day rose to its height in Girgenti. The sun, which hung directly over the town, poured down its light over everything, over the towers and roofs, stone streets, the sharp blue shadows, the walls and stairways. To the north I could see the white stretches of the hill on which the town stood, the white road leading up, with here and there a blackness where some cavern or sulphur shaft broke in, all beneath the

light of the sky, all lying complete and open under
the full noon. Somewhere in the town asses
brayed and market cries arose, hoarse, metallic;
they were more animal and wild than the braying
asses. From the barracks out beyond the Porta
Aurea burst out a chorus of soldiers singing.

In the bright daylight I could see the candles
and the little votive lamps burning in front of a
street shrine, set up for Easter; their flames were
saffron color and red as they wavered and seemed
somehow to hasten in the air. Then noon struck
and the bells of the town began to clang, raucous,
booming, shrill, and high, rumbling and clang-
ing everywhere, and most of all from the cathedral and San Giorgio, making the market criers
call the louder as they went along and setting
the near-by neighborhood of cocks to crowing.
The earth and the sun held everything. How
perfect, how brought to its last outline, how
single and immortal, it all seemed, the ancient,
dark and unforgetable life of the earth! Past
the temple of Zeus and the columns of Castor
and Pollux I could see the water of the bay
whitening shoreward in the sharp wind that had
sprung up from the south. And across the
street from where I sat a vender, who carried

under one shoulder a basket of fish and under the other a basket of melons and green herbs, put off his burden and lay down on the ground with his head on his elbow and fell asleep.

III

CULTURE AT DINNER

It was early twilight, just before the dinner hour, when I went into the garden and saw him there. He was standing by the wall, with one hand resting on it, looking out across the Fontebranda at the Duomo, whose black and white spaces now were buried in shadow and golden light. He was a young man, twenty perhaps, almost tall, fair, with a white, sensitive face that had long been beautiful with an intense ideal of living. I could see that as I stood in the doorway looking at him. And I could see also a hint of confusion somewhere about the eyes, a kind of glorious blur, a touch of the vagueness that might be in the face of a sort of academic young saint. He looked strong, athletic; but one of those strong Anglo-Saxon bodies that any fine dream can blow away. Plato, Francis Thompson, I figured, and perhaps the choruses of Æschylus would be his favorite reading.

He told me, when we fell into a conversation,

that he had finished college, Yale, great old place, that spring. And now travelling? Yes, with rather a definite purpose. So many fellows travelled just to do the grand tour before settling down. But he had felt the limitations of his education; as Callimachus said: μέγα βιβλόν, μέγα κακόν, much book, much evil; he felt that he needed more horizon. The idea was always troubling him that he had talked and studied and been lectured to about so many things that were still all in his head and meant nothing as a part of his real development. There were fine people at home, but they had never had a chance. He wanted an international quality added to what he already had. Not so much study and art perhaps, but seeing people, social contacts. And he wanted to see the things of Europe through the eyes of people, of men and women. And so he had thought it would be a good thing to come to a pension like this, where he might be on more direct terms with a group of people that hailed from all parts of the world. In a hotel it might take longer or might never happen. He meant to visit in this way a number of pensions to be found over Italy.

At last he had what he meant clear, and had

done speaking, and the excitement of stating his position quieted down a little from his eyes. Meanwhile I had stood there listening to what he said, liking the trouble he had in getting it out, liking the troubled eyes, the stress of spirit. But I listened with a sinking heart, for I was going over the list of guests who sat at our board just then. Perhaps this young seeker after culture had a vision of his own that he had brought with him, and was ready to throw over anything; perhaps there was a kind of golden light behind his mind that might fall over everything, as the light lay now soft and radiant over the streets, the highroad, the church towers. But in case he had not this softening splendor of his own, what then? The people who were to be at the table began to pass before me in the light of those young eyes I looked into.

The best of the lot was Signorina dell'Orto, and even at that my young friend would have to learn to know her. She was a new note ahead of him, that was true, but he would have to stretch for it. Signorina dell'Orto was a short little woman of fifty, who wore a short plain skirt, a man's collar and coat and cravat, and pulled her hair straight back. After meals, in

29

the drawing-room, she smoked a cheroot. She was very intelligent, and had been once the Italian tutor of the Czarina and later of German aristocratic families for twenty years before the war. She had been interned in Italy, shut up in a castle, in fact, for a year, on account of her free speech on the subject of the Allies. On her index finger she wore an old ring with some Austrian crest upon it. And for a Florentine she was unusually abrupt.

With her was her friend, a Miss Holtz, of twenty years' standing, as Miss Holtz loved to say, very German, long, tall, with prominent teeth. Between forty and fifty. Musical, rather maidenly, and flat.

At the head of the table sat a New York artist, with clear sharp features and white hair, alert, cool, like a cameo steeped in vinegar. Besides her were two Englishwomen in shirt-waists and a jangle of silver bracelets, who rattled like luxurious poodles when they entered the room but never said anything. Next to them came the young scion of a very old Roman house, sent by his mother to Siena, to get him out of Rome; but this young man, though he dressed very smartly, had at the time a cracked

head in a bandage, where a *Socialista* had hit
him with a stone during the last riot. He too
said nothing, but ate in silence and voraciously.
At the Roman's right sat Miss Ross, from Bir-
mingham, who ate almost nothing but biscuits
which she brought with her to the table. She
was one of those English daughters who have
been slaves to noble, aged fathers; but he was
dead now and she was left with an income, a
dozen photographs of him, and several rings that
he had given her on occasions. If she had been
a little less simple and dull and crotchety, one
might have blamed the father more for having
blotted her out so completely. But she was a
gentle creature who was always trying to divide
her English jam and tea with some one, whether
it was wanted or not. There was, besides all
these, an Italian doctor who was about to marry,
and who had such strict views on the position
of women that he had engaged an extra room
up-stairs where he and his wife were to dine
apart from the men of the table. He believed
on the whole in the harem system more or less,
and said, whenever marriage was mentioned,
that women should be locked in; which enraged
the New York artist and the English ladies to

outbursts that were fortunately beyond their
supply of Italian.

And finally, all the way round the table, at
the artist's left, came Professor and Mrs. Jurden,
from one of the two great universities of England.
Professor Jurden was a very tall man, sallow,
and very hesitant in his speech. He spoke so
slowly, in fact, that his wife used to tap him on
the back to get him through it, and she kept
this up in spite of his saying always, "Darling,
how often have I asked you not to do that?"
He had served in India in some sort of forestry
work, and during the war in South France hospi-
tals, where he had won a number of small bronze
medals but had completely ruined his health.
He spoke in a smothered voice with very impure
vowels, and always as if his teeth were sagging
and he feared to lose them if he left off holding
down his upper lip. His wife was tall, thin, and
wore her hair with a front of curls like Queen
Alexandra's. She spoke in a voice that she considered to be very soft and elegant, though,
as a matter of fact, it had lost all its bottom
tone and sounded all breath. She and Professor
Jurden were great liberals in their own estima-
tion, though not extreme, they hoped, in matters

where due thought was important before decisions were made. They had been in America for a few weeks on a government forestry report, but they regarded that country as most backward because their host in Georgia believed in the verbal inspiration of the Bible, incredible narrowness to their thinking; they regarded the Church of England as a just mean, neither too much nor too little, in religious theory. Mrs. Jurden and her husband disapproved of Italian cooking, exactly as they regarded Italians as cheats and liars, and went in for a vegetarian diet. At every meal she appeared at the table bringing cheese and a quantity of green stuff, lettuce, parsley, cress, and so on. Outside their rooms I used to see sometimes in the morning a straw waste-basket filled with strange leaves and stalks for the maid to carry away, as if they kept asses or goats privately in their quarters or were some secret creatures that browsed monstrously at night on plants and herbs.

I passed these guests of the pension through my mind in review as I stood listening to that boy from Yale with his beautiful face and fine dreams. I wondered what the dinner might be as I thought of what it had too often been.

A long golden shaft of light was falling on the
wall of the room when we took our seats at the
table. It struck the old faded walls and touched
the yellow hair of the newcomer, who had been
assigned a place between Miss Ross and the
Roman. But the golden sunbeam proved no
good augury, as I had hoped; for the dinner
began impossibly from the first course. Spinach
and eggs, but not enough of it. There was never
quite enough of anything, which was the incen-
tive that kept us all exact in our knowledge of
what every one there ate. The artist, out of
pure vexation at the sight of the small quantity
of food, took twice as much as she wanted. The
Roman, when his turn came, emptied the dish.
Was there more? Mrs. Jurden asked. Maria,
the maid, who was stupid and afraid of her mistress too, said that she did not know. Com-
plaints arose. Maria returned with another
platter one-fourth full. She brought a dish of
sliced salami to patch out. Dell'Orto said
scathing things, for she knew the *padrona's*
wiles. Chill penury had indeed repressed our
noble rage, the conversation sank to the lowest
levels of mere gross complaint; and so, to change
the tone of the occasion, for my countryman's

34

sake, I asked Professor Jurden how his Italian lessons were coming.

"But I am not taking lessons," he replied. "My wife is having them."

"I am tutoring with Don Paolo. I regard him as an excellent teacher, and enjoy our political discussions," his wife remarked.

Professor Jurden let his wife finish, looking at her thoughtfully the while, and then said that he had an Italian method he had devised for himself.

"What is that?" I asked, for I was having strenuous discipline under Don Paolo also, who laid on with all the more exuberance for being the author of my grammar.

"I am translating Shakespeare into Italian," Mr. Jurden said. "I figure that way I'll get a good vocabulary as well as learn the language by my own method."

"To begin with Shakespeare without knowing any Italian!" I exclaimed, astonished. Then I asked more quietly, "And are you putting it into verse also, Mr. Jurden?"

"How do you mean?"

"I mean, are you trying to reproduce the verse of the original?"

35

Professor Jurden looked at me puzzled for a moment. His wife tapped his back.

"Darling, I asked you not to do that."

"But the question was, dear," Mrs. Jurden went steadily on, "whether you were putting Shakespeare into Italian verse."

Professor Jurden turned to me: "Why? Is the original in verse?" he asked.

"Why, yes, but I'm afraid I don't understand what you mean," I answered, thinking that there must be something I had missed in his question.

"Why, I didn't know that Shakespeare's plays were in verse."

It was then that, like a foolish good American, I tried to help Mr. Jurden out and to make it easy for him; an Englishman, if I had said such a thing, would have treated me like a fool and the question as most American.

"But, of course," I said, "not all of Shakespeare is in verse. You mean that a great many of the speeches are in prose."

"Ah, that's probably why I never noticed it."

I looked away from Mr. Jurden to my idealist; he kept his eyes on his plate.

36

"I find Italian exceedingly easy," Mrs. Jurden observed; "I regard my progress as most encouraging."

At this the Signorina dell'Orto, who hated the Jurdens, turned to them. She understood some English but could not speak a word.

"*Cosa dice?*" she asked encouragingly, as if for mere information.

Mrs. Jurden undertook to put into Italian her ideas about the easy progress one made in the Italian language. Her remarks were, in the main, pauses and incredible mistakes, but the signorina was able to gather the general idea. Her face flushed red.

"Oh, yes," she began in a great man's voice, "the Italians will tell you that you are speaking very well. Don't believe them. I am always bored at these lies. A foreigner murders our language, but an Italian will say, 'Ah, you speak very well; you speak very well.'" She imitated the tone. "Well, I don't do it, I assure you. You just let an Italian go to England or Germany and you'll see. If he tries to ask a question in English they're so stupid they don't understand a word of it. They just look and say Baa, like fools." The signorina made a sound like a sheep

37

and twisted her head to one side. "Italians are too polite. It makes me furious."

"What a temper they have!" Mrs. Jurden said harshly to the New Yorker.

"Well," I thought, with my young dreamer in my heart, "he is learning. So much for cosmopolitan culture and politeness."

The Signorina dell'Orto was cooling somewhat now, for Mrs. Jurden began to make conciliations and to smile down from under that front of faded curls. But the signorina had not yet finished what she had to say.

"The difficulty in English is the pronunciation, which is so unintelligent. There is no way of learning it except as one does in a nursery, by hearing it. No rules, no anything but individual cases. How does one use one's mind in such an affair? And the grammar is for children too. It's simple enough for a child in arms. Italian has a grammar, thank God! Difficult, yes; but intelligent. It demanded intelligence to create Italian grammar and it takes intelligence to use it. You have no grammar in English."

Miss Ross looked up with no little asperity, for her.

"I'm sure I don't know what she means by

that," she said sharply; "I had a very good grammar."

The nature of this remark was so weak that even Mrs. Jurden saw it. A silence fell and lasted through the salad. Finally the New York artist, who had for some time been grumbling *sotto voce* to the Englishwoman about the shameless skimping in our food, to improve the quality of the occasion spoke to the young man.

"I'm sure you will find many delightful walks around Siena," she said. "Only this morning I was at San' Francesco. The altarpiece there is very interesting."

"I expect to find Siena very interesting," he replied in a conventional tone.

"And," Miss Ross added, gently, "there are two charming walks, one near Fontebranda and one toward Girasole. They are quite my favorites. I always take them. They are so like English lanes. Really Italy is lovely, isn't it? I often might believe myself in England; Father used to say the same."

The artist had enough of that subject, evidently!

"How much wood do you get now in a what do you call it — hecto, is it?" she asked Miss Ross.

"I'm afraid I can't tell you," Miss Ross answered, "I never light a fire; I detest hot rooms."

Mrs. Jurden finished making up her parcel of unconsumed green things and with that in one hand and her bottle of Marsala in the other, she rose from the table.

I had no wish to look into the eyes of the Yale lad; but I stole a glance as the company broke up. He was smiling bravely, trying to find his way through this new cosmopolitan world that he had been dreaming such fine things about. The signorina had taken out her cheroot and led the way to the drawing-room. I lingered a moment over my Vin Santo and then stole away up the little side stair to my room.

Through the closed shutters there I could see the boy standing again by the garden wall. His hand rested on it and his face was turned toward the Cathedral, on which one last light now delayed, at the very top. I had not enough courage to join him.

But I stood there hoping that he was one of those impenetrable idealists on whom the world makes no dents, who are never willing to believe that the actual can be true. The chambers in

40

the house of dreams are filled with so divine an air — And yet the fact remained that the international culture at that dinner-table had been rather actual. At least the first lesson might have been less stringent and wholesale. *L'idéal n'est que la vérité à distance*, I knew from Lamartine — surely there had been a time when this youth had wept with Lamartine— *À distance*, but how far? At how far distant must the ideal be to be the truth?

But as I stood there with my head against the shutter, meditating, I saw Mrs. Jurden appear and engage him in conversation.

"Look, do look, do you see?" she said. "The light on the Duomo, how charming it is! How charming! I should call it yellow. Would you? No, not exactly yellow. Well, orange. A sort of grayish orange. There, just at the top, do you see? How romantic Italy is! Are you going to stay long? Of course one longs for England. But we must have the change of climate. Look, do you see? I can't say I like the stripes in the Duomo. Do you?"

Mrs. Jurden had fallen into that particular brand of scenic monologue that English ladies sometimes revel in. I saw the face of the boy

41

turned quietly above the shadows of the Fontebranda toward the Cathedral. The black marbles of the tower had vanished from sight, leaving only the white, which seemed to hang there,
one above the other, with the spaces between, a
tower of white bands floating ineffably up and
up toward the topmost point.

"What a pity," Mrs. Jurden was saying, "the
Duomo was never completed! See there at this
end —" And the boy's gaze followed her pointing. He was getting architecture through Mrs.
Jurden's eyes.

IV

COUNTY MATTERS

MONSIGNORE, seven years before I knew him, had retired from active labor in the Church and had gone to live at the convent on the hill overlooking Rome. It was there, when the sisters took me in, that I used to walk and talk with him.

Monsignore was a man past sixty, not very tall, with a head bent slightly forward and black eyes twinkling out of a wise, grave little face. He smiled easily. And he had a way of looking at you with a quiet, kindly, steady gaze that ought to have routed you but did not do so, I finally decided, because it seemed somehow to be something rather eternal than personal. His hands were light and gracious.

One summer evening toward twilight, monsignore came out and joined me on a garden seat. Upward behind us ran the slope of the convent garden, cypress-trees and laurels, olives and a vineyard, and near at hand an ilex spreading

43

beyond the gravelled terrace. Below us, past the stone balustrade of the terrace and the long border of oleanders flowering now rose-colored and thick, the garden dropped down into the growing dusk of the city. And not far from where monsignore and I were sitting, a fountain came up, out of a round, low pool; the jet of it rose high into the air.

Monsignore had an odd twist about his mouth as he looked at me and something more than a twinkling in his eyes.

"How singular it is, signor," he began, having seated himself gravely and with a kind of permanent comfort in his arrangements, "I cannot rightly say I am surprised, because I am accustomed to this in them. Those English ladies, signor. We have been talking together in the *salone.* They are truly remarkable. They continue to surprise."

I inquired of Monsignore, though I might have guessed, what it was in these ladies that could still surprise and which of them he had in mind.

"All of them, no doubt," he said. "But the lady in particular was that Mrs. — I forget the name. I have the address she gave me, which

44

again I would not say surprised me, for I am accustomed to that also, but it has eight lines. The poor postmasters here in Italy no doubt would take it for a horoscope. However, what I was saying is that this dear lady was asking me about the princess who has just come in from Mantua — my country long ago, you may be so kind as to remember, signor, ah, long ago indeed, I'm afraid! The ladies came to me. They had heard, they said to me, that the new-comer was a princess. She was, I said, I used to know her father. 'Indeed?' they said." Monsignore gave a good imitation of false vowels and a choked throat, enjoying himself, as he went on, "'Really! And she has come here for a rest, no doubt.' She had come for a rest, no doubt, I said, and her name was one of the oldest in Italy. The ladies were interested at that. The history of these old Italian families is very jolly, my friend said. 'But still,' she said — and that was what did, I am afraid, sur-prise me a little — 'but still, my dear, of course, after all', she said, 'it's only an Italian title.'"

At this I smiled; the point of view was fa-miliar.

"'Of course it's not like our English titles.'"

Monsignore stopped with this quotation of the lady. He smoked in silence his cigarette.

The hills away beyond Rome were turning now to liquid amethyst. The superb golden brown of the palaces and walls glowed in the infinite, intense blue of the air. Below us we saw the descent of the Borghese Gardens, and saw the great city gates, the high walls above the Piazza del Popolo, the arches and high terraces, the long stairs leading down, magnificent saffron yellow, beyond the column of that heavy fountain plunging upward in the centre of the square. Rome, ageless, imperial, was there before us; the details of it and the whole of it came into my mind; it was rich, not too spiritual, not too chaste and early, but baroque, elaborated, full of security and sophistication and ornate power. Rome, that magnificent centre of magnificent time, with its palaces and worldly pomps, and its impenetrable permanence and cynicism. Rome, filled from place to place, at sudden turnings in the streets, in every quarter, with her eternal fountains.

Monsignore turned his eyes away from it.

"They are a fine people, no doubt, the English," he went on. "I have known so many of

46

them here in Rome — envoys, Oxford scholars, artists, fashionable travellers, aristocrats, and Catholic visitors — they come and go, my friend. And one way or another they are all alike. These ladies talking about the English titles are not very different, after all, from the rest."

"But how do you mean, monsignore?" I knew what he meant but it seemed better to inquire.

"Precisely this: they all bring England here with them. And they speak of Italy as one does with one's collection of objects. They regard Italy, and other countries I dare say, as put in the world to serve them and to express their so definite desires. And how very definite their desires are! Often so much more definite than discerning or exquisite — Signor, how can one be so specific as to the hour for tea and so satisfied with merely boiling one's food? But that, no doubt, is one of God's secrets. And if anything is different, then — when an Italian sees that some unimportant thing means so much to an Englishman and so little to him, he adapts himself. Naturally, since the whole consideration is chiefly business, he would not wish the gentleman to perish or go into a rage

47

for a simple matter of changing one's hours or leaving out all taste from a sauce. And thus, my friend, a country begins to conform to English ways.

"The British Isles are evidently a diverse climate from ours, are they not? But I have heard Englishmen here complain of the hours of the museums. They complain of the length of the postal cards. Every Sunday when the good sisters give us the *gelati* do you not mark the lady who says regularly there is no ice-cream like Buzzard's ice-cream? And ah, she says, there are no peaches like English peaches! And the gentleman near you at dinner, the Cambridge professor who has been studying at Pesto and Capua, you have heard him insist that the eggs here in Rome are undernourishing? They look like eggs, he says, but he finds that they have no sustenance in them. Eggs!"

I nodded and smiled, for I remembered the egg criticisms and I wished to keep monsignore going.

"What do you think, signor? Do you not think that this all follows from their great individualism? I don't mean originality, which springs from some unique and powerful centre, does it

48

not? I mean mere subdivisions of oneself. I mean that one divides rather than distinguishes." I chuckled to see the gracious, firm hand tap the knee lightly.

"If one clings so subtly to oneself, naturally one may cling in the same way to one's country and its ways, no? *Ma che*, they are inner! What special attachments they have to their pipes, their umbrellas; and I am told they give names, Little Mary, Bess, and so on, to covers for the bed, and derive much humor from the fact. What special little affairs of the heart they hold with ferns and daffodils and little garden flowers! And how they must know which tree is which and what to call every plant one sees! And what a stew they make about the love of the country! One wonders from their manner when they speak of the country how they explain to themselves our Italian *villeggiatura*, the months that Italians who can afford it pass every year in the country. And what do they make of our habit of gardens, since we have so few garden sentiments, so few gentle privacies with columbines and primroses? And what trysts the English affect to keep with squirrels, birds, ants, and wild fowl, may God help me! It is

49

so hard for me to understand! How, I ask my-self, do such people ever arrive at clear concep-tions, at outlines, at the relations of things?

"Signor, it is the same — is it not? — with their religion. They specialize in it, each and every one almost; in Britain there is an annual crop of creeds and cults."

I quoted rather obviously, more to keep the spell working, "The land of three hundred reli-gions and one sauce."

"So. But" — monsignore rubbed his hands gleefully together — "is it not a droll thing, signor, how these Northern nations, who have such pious strength in their inmost selves, should feel so much the need of stimulants? What floods of tea these English ladies drink!"

After that little thrust monsignore quieted into something graver that flared his nostrils for half a second.

"It's not only that they bring their personal convictions into foreign lands. They not only dress for dinner, have their hours for tennis, and import English biscuit into the very heart of a Chinese desert. They bring all this into the Church. What a time we have with our converts, signor! They take everything so hotly. They consider that one cannot have too much zeal. And so they search their souls and rend themselves. And they naturally infer that they can do the same to us. They want to specialize on every point. But the Church, signor, was not born in a day, and it teaches the sin of scrupulosity. Not to speak of egos, may I say that one's inner voice may be a little overweening?

"And may I tell you about one of these converts, a remarkable man, too? It was when I was at the head of one of the Vatican colleges here in Rome, fifteen years ago. This gentleman came of one of the oldest English families, I am told, an old county family, a great name. Well, signor, it is clear that when he came into the Church he came with the profoundest of inner convictions, let us admit that. I have no doubt he broke down half a dozen priests in the process. And so, once in, he studied everything, he gave money most liberally, and he gave his criticisms, his personal opinions, and his advice at the same time.

"I had invited this gentleman to visit us in the country at our villa near Tivoli; the college had a villa there. One week-end in the summer he came out. How well I remember it! He

51

was a handsome man, tall, lean, cranky-looking
perhaps, but distinguished. He came on a
Saturday. He arrived from the station in a
carriage, and behind him came a sort of van
with his two servants and a huge pile of boxes
and bundles. At first I thought he must have
mistaken the invitation; you see, I had asked
him for over Sunday. However, there he was,
with the boxes and bales and parcels and the two
servants! But no, he had that clear, it was for
Sunday; and we were soon walking in the garden,
discussing the problem of Catholic education,
while his servants were up-stairs, as I learned
afterward, making no end of trouble about the
arrangement of the rooms. At dinner that night
— you won't believe me, signor, when I tell you
— that night at dinner I sat at the head of our
long table of forty or more young fellows and my
distinguished visitor of course sat at my right.
But after grace was said what should I see, bless
my soul, but the man servant, who came down
the entire length of the refectory, past the entire
line of seminarians at table, with a tray full of
bottles and other objects! These he brought
and offered to his master, to none of the rest
of us, and my guest made his selection from

them, putting things beside his plate in the most particular manner. There were Chutney, curry, sauces, and what not. He then resumed the conversation as if all this were a mere matter of course. The man servant went back to the kitchen then to supervise the cooking of his master's meat. Next morning he was there about boiling eggs.

"But, dear signor, all that was nothing to the way my guest kept his eye on me and the ritual! I remember how he remained in the sacristy while I was preparing for the mass. You see, as I went out of the door I brushed against a curtain and, as one would, raised my hand to my head. After mass he was waiting for me. 'And why did you touch your beretta like that,' he asked, 'entering the church? I never knew that that was in the ritual!'"

Monsignore made a little salute with his hand.

"And yet he was a very devout, distinguished, liberal gentleman."

"I can easily believe that also," I replied. "But, monsignore, I often wonder what you Italians do think of us foreigners. You are, at the same time, so polite and so astute."

"Well, how the Italians get around this prob-

lem of the English I can at least tell you, signor."

"How is that?" I asked.

"The Italians solve it; they think they're all
crazy."

Monsignore smiled gently after this, but did
not add that the Italians were doubtless mistaken. I would forgive him for talking so much,
he said. But I must admit that he was not
always so garrulous. Old age and English ladies had made him so to-day. And yet when one
reflects — he began again.

Aye, aye, aye, what an odd world it was!
Take the Frenchmen. The Frenchmen that he
had known had been delightful gentlemen.
They had every one of them been deferential,
suave, affable, complaisant. Not always *sim-
patico* but yet always agreeable personally. A
little mannerism undoubtedly. But no affectation. Where a Frenchman was mannered an
Englishman was affected; with him it went
further inward. Every Englishman he had
known, monsignore said, had affected something;
if he had no other pose he underposed. But not
a Frenchman, for all his airs and graces. So far
as he knew the French, at least, this opinion of

them he found true. The Frenchmen he had
known did no foolish things, that is to say, freakish, cranky things; they posed externally if they
posed at all. But then if you got a crowd of
them together, every one knows what happens.
They act like fools. Every one knows of the
fights in the Paris Chamber, the deputies throwing ink-bottles and rushing together with their
fists.

On the other hand, take a set of Englishmen.
No matter how freakish any single one of them
may be, no matter how many hobbies and poses
they have among them, the whole meeting is
ruled by common sense.

"How they do it," monsignore went on, "I
don't know. But they do. The soul of good
sense. I sometimes think the English are the
greatest race among human beings, because they
are most like the universe. In the universe
every single thing has its own ways, its own
traits, inexhaustibly diverse, endlessly individual, and yet the whole taken together has
its good order and sense. However, I'm Latin
enough to protest that the latter is the more
permanent and more important side of the universe. I mean order, sense, idea. But I am

being fanciful, perhaps. What is it that gives Englishmen this common sense and order when you take them in a body? Is it athletics or born sanity — that would be hard to believe, that last! — or is it a long training in government and a governing class?" Monsignore looked at me slyly.

"Or is it, signor," he added, "that where there are so many individualisms one sees the necessity of a general concession to the group? Either of playing the game together or of disaster?"

"But how do you figure all this, monsignore?" I asked, hoping piously for light on a question I often turned in my own head. "All our Anglo-Saxon talk about baths, say, or about justice, about truth?"

"Perhaps," monsignore ventured — with a smile that my old pastor at home would have called Jesuitical, I am sure — "perhaps strong beasts make strong cages." I said I got the point.

"Dear signor," he said presently, "we can say this if nothing else: the English never give up the county point of view. The strength of the English lies in their ability to carry the county over the world."

56

In the wind the spray from the fountain blew out past the rim and on to the gravel with a sound like swift retreating rain. The cypresses near by moved also in the wind; the swaying columns of their black masses and the swaying column of the fountain rose together upward. From somewhere on the shadowy slope behind, a bird began to sing; its voice was like starlight, like a pipe, like a cry; it made a long bright line across the darkness.

Monsignore presently began again; he was to talk his thoughts through.

"As for me, signor — and I have wondered sometimes how much deep down that would be true of my country — I have the weakness of the long vista. The malady of horizons, I have, aye, aye, signor. I lack strength, from old age perhaps and perhaps from a little universality of mine. That is to say, the county, la provincia, where I was born — and even Italy — slips out of my mind, signor. I tend to follow reason; and to me reason is the kind of imagination that perceives the relation to one another of all things, how they check or support one another, the relation, signor, of all things in our world about us and in our world of time. And

57

my mind possesses strength and peace only through renouncing what is impossible and co-operating with what is necessary. Do I make a sermon? Perhaps I miss my old profession, my dear. A long history is ours, signor, and I sit here in Rome and look at things, not so much as they seem when they pass before me but as they remain when they are over."

We were silent, and monsignore with his light hand began to tap a cigarette on his case. He gave a little chuckle.

"Spinoza said something like that — magnif-icent heretic, I whisper it to you, signor — he should live in Rome. I'm afraid we should have made very sorry colonizers, Spinoza and I, signor."

We sat on for a while, and I saw far down be-low us the innumerable lights coming slowly out. The day was ended, and in the quarter nearest us the city had grown quieter. The hills, the domes, the great houses and walls loomed against the glow of the streets and against the blue, intense, wide sky. After a time my com-panion rose and went over to the balustrade and stood looking down. He spoke to me at length, without turning.

"Do you know, signor, sometimes I could believe that even in this place one can hear the fountains of Rome."

V

MENTAL GOODNESS

WE had all three descended from the same train, though from different compartments, and gone to the same hotel, the San Marco; and had been crossing one another's paths all day. And after luncheon I had seen the Englishman in carpet slippers sitting with his feet up on a chair in the *salone*, very much at home. The Frenchman had been there also, at the other end of the room, going over a portfolio of paintings and sketches that a porter had brought up from the station. But we had not spoken to each other. And then that evening at the café under the arcades of the piazza we drifted together. Our table was by one of the columns and near a flowering oleander, pale rose. A rumble of rich voices in Tuscan and Romagnolo was everywhere.

The two men had already begun a conversation when I joined them, and I sat observing them a long while in silence.

The Englishman turned out to be a fellow in

history at some Oxford college. He was a big
man with a burly front and red eyebrows; but
you could see that secretly his being swam in
sentiment, a ruddy giant with a heart of mush.
He might swear gruffly enough but would fall in
love with the first ringlet curl. And the thought
that in his own way he was almost certain to
love poetry, made you forgive him much. An
odd mixture of boorishness, brains, and inno-
cence he was, evidently, all signs considered.
He had a way of not answering when the
Frenchman expected him to; and toward both
of us he manifested that huffiness of manner that
so often accompanies English culture, a trait that
puzzles unendingly the well-bred of other lands,
and is the more puzzling for being followed
later so often by a devotion and an outpour of
confidences equally beyond foreign ideas of
breeding.

The Frenchman was a painter, a shrewd little
man; climbed up from out some parental shop
on the boulevards, very likely. I had seen some
of his paintings that afternoon in the *salone*.
He was one of those busy French artists who
seem to paint with milk under a magnifying-
glass smooth, creamy pictures with too much

brown in the shadows, bourgeois, as apt and pat as a toilet-soap; work that makes no furor, but sells, flowing to its own level as easily and gratefully as water. His hair was cropped close and his eyes were gray and clear. He spoke English very well.

I scarcely noted what the two were saying; they were talking about Ravenna, I heard that much. And one of them talked as much as the other, though the Englishman had a look that said: "Behold, I am taciturn. I belong to a strong, silent race." I observed this vaguely as my thoughts wandered out from the company and the glass of *Certosa verde* to the piazza around me and to Ravenna.

After seven years Ravenna was more beautiful than ever. The war had waked it up somewhat; there was a new trades-union government arising and a new public market, and Byron's palace, repainted a single gray over everything, had become the headquarters for co-operative labor; but all that scarcely left a ripple. How Ravenna differed from Vicenza or Siena or Perugia or Florence: I was turning that question over in my mind. I thought of the quiet and romantic and warm quality of it; how the ro-

62

mance of Ravenna is deepened beyond that of
Venice, which it is most like, by the basilicas, by
the Byzantine and Roman, and by that pine
forest between the town and the sea, whose
lights and shadows make a part of the very air.
And of the streets I thought, half deserted, with
their yellow and brown and rose and white and
blue houses, faded now; long streets like canals,
constantly varied like the streets of Venice by
the shifting and turning of the lines of direction
they take, but made more beautiful still by the
delicate, changing levels of their ground. The
tombs and basilicas, romantic with an old solitude, stand apart, lonely and quiet and open,
glowing with mosaic and carrying in their
painted capitals the richest element of antique
art, its color. Even the antiquities of this town
are its own, they are like none elsewhere.

The night was coming down as we sat there.
The old palaces of the piazza above their arcades
were a soft rose-color against the deep blue of
the sky, in which the stars were shining, near
and golden and sharp. A kind of blue clearness
still showed along the ground below. Then I
realized all at once that the Frenchman was
asking me a question.

"How many years was it, monsieur, that Byron lived in Ravenna? Neither of us remembers. Do you know?"

"Two years," I replied. "Byron thought Ravenna the most beautiful city in Italy."

"Indeed, monsieur? How interesting to hear that! Perhaps I should agree with him — almost, not quite. I had thought that it might have been his love for the Contessa Guiccioli that kept him here. How interesting it is, messieurs, that of all women she at last could keep Byron's love, I have so often thought that! Monsieur here was saying — just what was it you were saying, monsieur? I am too stupid to remember it clearly."

"I was saying," the Englishman repeated, "that Byron led a wild life in Venice, hit it up; there was something about it desperate in a way, do you see? But in Ravenna he seems to have settled down, do you see?"

"The influence of the Contessa, monsieur," said the painter.

"Somewhat. And other causes. Personally I'm not one of those who censure Byron harshly. There are people who won't read his poems, or won't praise them, because of his life, all the

business of women, cynicism, satire on established order. Seems to me a foolish attitude.
I always maintain we can jolly well admire
Byron's genius without approving of his life."
The Englishman blushed, and paused; he was
doubtless quite ashamed of such an attempt to
express himself clearly.

The painter made no reply and the Englishman went on.

"I'm convinced on that point, by George!
And I'm always reminded that there were a
thousand things in Byron's life that might excuse
his conduct. Circumstances were often against
him, poor chap!"

"*Excuse,* monsieur?" the Frenchman interrupted. "How, *excuse?*"

"Why, I mean to say we all know Byron's
life, what it was ——"

"Certainly."

"But that shouldn't blind us to his merits as
a poet, do you see? Byron had eloquence and
great mental vigor. He has an infinity about
him like the sea, as one of our critics says, the
poet Swinburne ——?"

"Ah, yes, Swinburne, to be sure, monsieur."

"Well, if that be so, we ought to be able to

overlook his failings in the light of his achievements, if you see what I mean."

I thought the Frenchman's eyes looked a little glaring, but he made no answer.

"What's more, the accounts are probably exaggerated."

"Grant they are true, monsieur," the other said. "What difference does that make? It is the same. I am not sure I *do* see what you mean. Perhaps it is that Frenchmen do not understand very well the Anglo-Saxons, not always; how should one race understand another? But why should we forgive Byron, may I ask again?"

"I mean that the English race" — the Englishman's voice grew tender as if he were speaking of a beloved brother — "is a just race. By God, I believe we have a great desire to be human, to make allowances; justice is an Englishman's passion!"

"What very odd passions the English have, monsieur!"

"Yes; justice —" the Englishman repeated.

"But, monsieur, I should put justice down as engaging for the intellect, a love-affair of the brain, monsieur."

66

"Naturally I don't mean to say that other races may not be just and human also."

"I think, monsieur," the Frenchman replied, ignoring the concession quite as his little flippancy had just been ignored, "that there may be a difference after all. I should never understand very well this passion for forgiving a great poet like Byron because his poetry is great."

"It may jolly well be that the French genius is harder," the Englishman said — "the *esprit de logique*."

"That may be. But why forgive or make excuses? Can that help Byron or make him greater?"

"But it praises Byron's genius without endorsing his conduct."

"Ah, I see. I see. We might say it preserves our greatness and Byron's also. That is it, is it not?"

"If you like."

There was a long pause. Then the Frenchman went on:

"We protect our own standards, but also we confess that under the circumstances we should act the same as Byron did. It is droll."

"Not entirely," the Englishman objected.

67

"Ah, well, to our *mouton*. Let us see. Byron is great, in some respects he differs from us — in theory at least we differ from him, if not always in conduct. Very well. In spite of his differing from us he is a great poet. Therefore we forgive him. You forgive him, monsieur?"

"Oh, rather, I should say I do. Though I can't say that of all my friends; there are some who hold out against him."

"Exactly. And I see no need of forgiving him at all, and such is life."

"But, I mean, why be harsh in judging Byron? I always say," the Englishman persisted.

"That's one sort of good, perhaps, monsieur. To forgive is, as you say, very kind, very tender, very just and human. It has a sort of piety in it, perhaps."

The Englishman added: "Rather!"

"Ah, yes, monsieur, and it is also easier. For if we make allowances for Byron, and pardon him a little, we do not have to re-examine our own system, *n'est-ce pas?*"

The Englishman made no answer.

"But there is another sort of goodness, we think, monsieur — what I may call mental goodness."

"Mental goodness?" The Englishman filled another pipe with steady determination.

"Exactly, monsieur: mental goodness, the goodness of understanding. I believe that instead of 'forgiving' Byron, as you say, it is better to understand the facts. That seems to me kinder, ah, much kinder! We may not of course enjoy it so much as we might enjoy forgiving" — he looked up to see if his little thrust had gone home, but his listener sat masked in repose — "and it may be more disturbing than making allowances might be or altering history to suit ideals. You know the French phrase, I am sure, monsieur: 'the defect of one's excellence'?"

"Certainly."

"That is what we mean by it. Byron's violence and extremes were part of that quality that swept his poetry along. His weakness with women was the defect of the excellence that made him a lyric poet. Biology, no doubt, monsieur. One accepts this as one accepts the fact that fire is beautiful but burns one. It is an extreme, it is regrettable. But the flame is an extreme as much as the burning is."

A sound of a bell far away, from off toward

San Vitale, came to our ears, beautiful and soft. The little painter began to speak more vehemently.

"Is not this kinder in the end, monsieur, to make the head to see straight than to depend on the humors of the heart?"

He turned to me when the Englishman said nothing: "To keep the heart in the head, that is better than so near the digestion, which has not the so good constancy. Ah, but the stomach has temperament, has it not?"

"Very much so," I agreed.

"But what do you think, monsieur?" he turned to me. "You have been silent. What do you think of all this in America?"

"In America," I said, "we are still in the forgiving stage also. Our biographies are usually the refinement of lying. We take Rousseau's advice literally: *Commençons par écarter tous les faits.* Or we manage a sort of blinking, with pity. For example, take our favorite story-writer; he was in prison two years for taking money in a bank. But we don't like to admit it. We deny it, or we soften the facts. I know a man whose desk was next to this writer's. He saw the whole business at the start and

70

warned the offender. But it did no good. The thieving went right ahead. The man tells me the three things the money was needed for were the support of the writer's wife — who was ill and to whom he was devoted — playing poker, and digging for a buried treasure down by the river."

"I see, monsieur. And you mean that these same traits are behind this author's stories?"

"Just that," I said; "the gentleness and kindness and adventure and daredevil and romance in his stories all came out also in this love for his wife, for gambling, for treasure-hunting, and so strong that they made him steal."

"But also they made him create his art, monsieur."

"Ah, but to admit that," I said, "people must be ready to look into their own scheme of values a little, art and business, money, happiness, goodness. It's pleasanter to do the other, to be evasive or merciful."

"Exactly. It is sweet to be forgiving, is it not, monsieur? But it is intelligent and permanent to be understanding."

He turned to the Englishman, smiling and making another little thrust: "The defect of

71

one's excellence is not a sacred phrase, perhaps, but it is the kindest in the world."

The Englishman looked off into the blue night, untouched by all this patter, and still silent. The Frenchman looked at me with a bit of a shrug, as if to say, "*Espèce de type anglais, non?*" Then the other took his pipe from his lips and said:

"The English nature is a compassionate and tender one."

The Frenchman looked at him a moment.

"Ah, yes, we know that from your ballads," he said.

The conversation was ended by the *padrone's* coming up with our bill. The café was already deserted, the voices gone, and most of the piazza lights were out. The Englishman paid, waving us brusquely aside, and a bit proudly, it seemed to me, as if to put the Frenchman in his place, and he and the painter rose to go.

The *padrone* made a bow. The signor was from Byron's country, he said in Italian. Byron was a great poet, they had named a piazza for him in Ravenna. He himself knew many of Byron's verses in English, but if he were to try to pronounce them, it would make to laugh.

e wished the signori good night and golden
ms.

et the two men set off and stayed on there
after the doors of the café were shut; and
now and then passers-by crossed the piazza;
now and then the footsteps of the watchman
ame from a far corner. I smiled a little to
think of the irony of how we had all sat there
together; how none of us had mentioned a word
of it, and yet the beauty and reality of the time
and place had laid its finger, nevertheless, on
the invisible sources of our talk and the shy
accents of our vehemence.

The stars looked closer now and more golden
in the deep blue of the air. Against the blue
and the stars rose the figure of St. Mark's lion
on the column near by and the pointed Venetian
battlements along the palace walls. A soft
night breeze had set in from the Adriatic and
stirred the oleander branches. The strange,
bitter fragrance of the blossoms spread abroad,
and the stirred leaves made a little clicking
sound. Otherwise there was no sound anywhere.
Ravenna was as silent as night on water.

Then from the next piazza, over by Dante's
tomb and Byron's palace, a guitar struck up

73

and a man began to sing.   It was a wild, metal
voice, and all the brighter for the stillness a
the stone streets on which it fell.   I could
the strumming of the guitar, the voice sin
and the stir of branches near me.   I could
the pale curves of the arcades, and the ro
color glowing on the walls in the dim light of th
few street-lamps below, and darkening into mere
shadow higher up against the deep sky.   And
close at hand, almost overhead, I saw the shapes
of the leaves, the most beautiful in the world.
I thought of Byron and his life at Ravenna,
the love, the revolution, the proud and lonely
and ironical isolation, and of Dante.   The night,
the straight lines of the column with its lion's
wings, the rumor of the sea in the soft wind,
the memory of these great men, the music, and
the quietness seemed all one thing, seemed complete and perfect as one of the oleander leaves.
And with them, after a fashion, went also the
slight little Frenchman with his clear, wise
phrase.

VI

PROVIDENCE IN FLORENCE

For our first day in the pension on the Arn
the only other guest at our table was an American young lady. We had been told that the
other guests were out for the day. But both
my friend and I were so worn with the table
amenities of our Siena headquarters that we
felt like holding to a prudent silence. I had
had all too much of inane travel anecdotes, of
the weather, of impressions of Italian oddities,
of daily experiences and future plans, of gossip,
personal inquiry, feuds, teas, and antiqua-
rianisms. With the help of God, I planned, as
Benvenuto Cellini said when he had murdered
the man, to make my escape; I meant in this
new pension to be polite, precisely that. And
so we were seated, my friend and I, said good
evening carefully, and busied ourselves with the
dinner. Two courses passed and only a few
murmurs between my friend and me. Then the
young lady, who had been looking us over
through the *antepasto* and the *minestrone*, took

the situation in hand and wholly shamed us. She looked up and smiled at us and said:

"How long will you gentlemen be in the city?"

I started. "In the city!" Who would ever have thought of that for Florence? My thoughts took on a plush lining and shook with Pullman car springs. And "you gentlemen"! But I replied that we hoped to be there for some time.

"I see you are from the States, are you not?" she went on with the straight manner of a war girl, evidently. "I am in the Red Cross here."

We explained ourselves and that we were travelling. She was a tall girl with auburn, crimpy hair; honest freckles sprinkled on the bridge of her nose; a little dip downward in the middle of her upper lip; and a figure in a long high corset like Queen Mary's. She had a quick, staccato way of talking, slightly indistinct even to an American.

We made exchanges in the obvious. Then, shortly afterward, the happy mention of antiques and of buying in general started us all off, at the beginning at least, together. The young lady, it developed, drew her salary, and also her allowance, in American money, which she

turned into lire at twenty-two on the dollar.
That made her rich beyond her dreams. She
was thrilled with the buying. Did you ever see
anything like it in your life? Wasn't it terrible
in Italy? What did you think she had paid for
this dress? Sixteen dollars, made on Via Torna-
buoni! Her house at home, in Providence, was
very plain, just mission furniture and blue and
white curtains, not bad, but, you know, so many
houses in Providence were like that. And so
she was buying all sorts of things, and auntie
would be delighted.

It appeared that she had bought a hat for two
dollars and had found copies of all her favorite
pictures at the print shop for ten lire each, less
than fifty cents. After dinner she showed us
cigarette cases, majolica, lace, table linen, filet,
cameos, frames, pictures, mosaics, every sort of
thing. The whole litter of it showed no taste,
but there was a sort of happy possessive look
to it that was pleasing enough to see. The
exhibition lasted most of the evening, as object
after object was drawn from one trunk after
another. She could give us the name and the
street for every dealer connected with them;
and I perceived that she had orders out all over

Florence and seemed to have her lace-makers, wood-carvers, milliners, jewellers, and book-binders, like a great Medici princess.

Sometimes, she confessed, she did not like the things afterward so much as she had liked them when she was buying. However — as she said — And so the exposition went on.

The next day at luncheon the conte appeared.

The conte was a man past thirty, compact, alert, almost short in stature, with auburn hair and mustache. His eyes were quick and gray; his clothes were smart but a little worn; and he wore on his right hand a sardonyx ring with arms. His beautiful, rapid Sennese was clear as a pattern in a book and recklessly elegant and witty. The conte's name was one of the oldest in Italy, and his arms were scattered over all Rome by one of the popes that had come from his family.

The conte bowed and wished every one a good evening as he sat down at the table, and explained that he had been absent in Siena, where he had gone to look after a palace that had been left him by his ancestors, damp, dark, with one caretaker and thirty-eight apartments, and fit for nothing but growing mushrooms.

"One wears these palaces exactly as one wears this ring," he added, holding up his right hand, "but the ring is less trouble. I shall try to leave nothing but rings and bank stock behind me. Let us be modern!"

He relapsed then into his *ravioli*, after a glance at the Red Cross young lady, who was plainly about to begin an account.

She began to tell me about her life, official so to speak, in Florence. She was in the office at the top of Berchielli's all day. But there was every sort of thing to be done; people to be found; connections established between members of families; pension money sent to the right people. Then there were inquiries to go to Washington, and goodness knows when you got an answer and the people coming every day and making a row. There were all sorts of passport troubles for old people who wished to go to America, and for ex-soldiers who had leave from the American army to visit their parents in Italy and who were trying to dodge the clutches of the Italian army. And then at four you had tea sent up from the hotel and went shopping. Sometimes on Saturday nights, the young lady said, she'd run off to Rome to see her friends in the office there, taking the midnight express and getting back for Monday morning. And whenever she heard of a festival in the near-by towns, she went. They were adorable, the procession at Grassina and the festival she had seen at Montepulciano, where they led a little child dressed in white, with a golden wig and a wreath of flowers, like a little angel, and standing on an ass, right down the valley into the town and into the church and up to the altar. She had even been to Paestum, where she had spent the night in a peasant's house. She half expected to be murdered, but they brought out a prize ham and cut it in her honor. She had gone to tell them about their son; for they could not read at all the information sent them in English from Washington, and nobody in the village could read it, but the priest knew that it was English. Wasn't it absurd how, no matter how many kicks were sent in, those people in Washington went right on sending papers in English all over Italy? Why did Washington do this? She loved the church, though they seemed like pagans and auntie would be shocked. And she adored walking up through the Porto San Giorgio to hear the nightingales when the moon

80

was out. There was another bird, too, besides the nightingale. A deeper note. She wondered what it was and looked inquiringly at the conte, who made a wry face and shrugged his shoulders. Did not the conte know birds? Surely every one loved birds. She had asked every Italian she saw, but none of them knew. They just said *Ma che*, it was a bird! Weren't they queer? Look how many things they called just *machina*, typewriter was *machina*, and so was — well, ever so many things. Her uncle knew every bird in New England. And all the ferns, too, for that matter. Alfano, her Florentine friend, often went with her; he had been thirteen months in prison in Austria and was so interesting. It was so interesting getting to know the real Italian nature this way!

The conte listened and looked at me, and his clear eyes flickered for half a second; but he said nothing. She turned to him:

"Oh, conte, you have such a wonderful country," she said radiantly, "I simply love it."

"We are fortunate that you help to make it so," he answered with a little bow to her. "What extraordinarily happy lives American ladies lead, *cara signorina!*"

81

THE THREE FOUNTAINS

"Do we?" answered the young lady, and the luncheon ended on rather that note.

Dinner, when it came round that night, proved not to be for those that dream international dreams of harmony and eternal understanding. Two ladies had arrived in the afternoon and had been seated at our table next to the plump little Austrian baroness, who had been absent for the day in the too sweet environs, as she called them. One of the arrivals was from New York, a miniature-painter, with clear features and firm, sharp motions that suggested a Colonial door-knocker. Beside her sat the Irish lady, whom she had met a day or two before in Perugia.

"I'm always meeting people this way," she told me later; "it's amusing to see what they are like, if you don't have to keep it up." This Irish lady had thick gray hair like a powdered wig, round eyes far apart, and flattish nostrils, round and wide. "A Louis Quinze mule!" the conte said to me later, when we too were better friends.

At the beginning of the dinner, while the anchovy *antepasto* was served, the painter, merely by way of conversation, I think, asked in her cool, clear voice:

82

"Miss Townshend, I suppose of course you are a Home Ruler?"

"You do?" Miss Townshend put down her fork and roared at her friend with a huge voice and a manner like a stump orator. "Did you ever hear of a Townshend who was a Home Ruler?"

A pause.

"Did you ever hear of a Townshend who was a Catholic?"

A pause, and this time silence in the whole dining-room, to hear what the lady was roaring about in this fashion.

"Did you ever hear of a Townshend who was a —— ?"

"I never heard of a Townshend," the painter interrupted, coolly, and went back to her anchovies.

The dining-room in its turn went back to its clatter, while an awkward silence reigned at our table.

But the Providence young lady had not worked for nothing with consuls and parents and Latin officials.

"Why, I'm sure I've heard of lots of Townshends," she said, and added enthusiastically, "some of them were historical heroes, weren't they?"

Miss Townshend lowered her voice a little as she answered, "If they spell it with an h, madame, I think I may say they were."

The conte saw the point of the American young lady's efforts with this hardened old clay of Europe, and joined in gaily toward the peace basis. He had already had two round goblets of Capri Bianco.

"I have no doubt of that," he said. "And speaking of heroes," he began, "now what's one's idea of a hero? How many ideals there are! Now my ideal is a man like Nerino Gamba. You have not heard of him? But he is known as a financier, a patron of the arts, an impresario, a director of theatres, a prince."

"Indeed?" I asked. "Where is he — in Rome?"

"No, just now he is in the prison at Volterra." The Europe represented smiled. The young lady from Providence started, her eyes stretched a little. But she had the air of having seen these Italians before. She even managed to say, not "in prison," but only "Volterra?"

"Yes, signorina, quite. For forging checks."

"Forging checks?"

"That is the way he started his fortune. This is the way he used to do it: He would find out a very rich man, one with a name that could be duplicated of course, some not unique name, and then he would get a secretary with the same name. In Italy, that is easy, we have so many names; if one is named for half a dozen saints, one may select among them. He would have his secretary write out checks and these he would cash. And since he was a great and rich person no one thought of making trouble for him for a long time. One can arrange, you know, signorina. He changed secretaries when there was need for more money some time or other, and got thus another rich man's name. In this way he became very rich and bought up many objects of art. Have you not heard of the Crivelli that he has, that they tried to buy in America? At any rate he loved the theatre and so financed a great many companies, and gave the actresses whom he loved magnificent gifts. And now that he is caught they have all had to give the things up to be sold for the creditors, is it not terrible, poor women! All but Mimi Grammatica, she was more fortunate; he had given

85

her only money, fifty thousand lire, and she had spent it all, and now they could not get any of it back from her. It is droll. It reminds me of Epictetus' advice to philosophers to study sheep, who do not spit up again the grass they eat, but turn it into hides and wool. That Mimi did, though she is no sheep, I assure you, and what a great actress she is! Nerino Gamba has been in prison two years now — they had to do something about it of course, but he was given only three years. He is planning now for several fine companies in the theatres, directing them from prison, and he will soon be out and making his career again. Now that is what I call a hero!"

The Red Cross young lady looked at him blankly.

"Why not, *cara signorina?* He has brains, power, imagination, daring, taste. What would you have?"

"But of course you are only joking," she laughed.

"Oh, no, no, no, no, not at all!" the conte waved his hand with the ring on it, "I assure you. This man is like Machiavelli, the intention, the cool mind."

The young lady's face became very serious.

"Oh, if you really mean it, conte," she said, "I can't let you go on thinking like that. It's so cynical."

"Exactly, *cara signorina*, it is cynical. It is Continental," the conte replied gravely. "It is Italian. We are a cynical race, we have three thousand years of history behind us."

"How too romantic!" said the baroness, but the conte kept his eyes on the young lady. The honest young face looked troubled and slightly indignant; this sort of problem that cannot be changed by believing in the best was not to her taste. She thought a moment.

"Well, I just don't understand Italians," she said then, "but I suppose I never shall do that. It just shows that America is the place for me after all."

"On the contrary," the conte answered, bowing again, "let us hope that you can be in both, in both countries and at the same time even, like the holy Apostles."

"Our pastor used to explain this ubiquity of the Apostles to my mother and me," the baroness interposed, "but I could never quite understand it."

"But, baroness," the conte replied, "the Apostles were saints, and that explains anything." He turned again to the Providence young lady.

"Well, I don't quite understand even my friends in Italy," she said, now very serious. "Now even Alfano, he is different from my ——"

"Oh, Alfano?" the conte interrupted. "Ah, I know Alfano. And I know his ex-wife. But how beautiful the moon is from San Giorgio!"

"His wife? Why, is he married?" the girl asked quickly.

"Alfano *was* married. He is not married now, *cara signorina*. That is to say, he is not wholly married."

I could see that this was a great shock to her, but her frontier American control, or whatever good thing it was, helped her to go straight ahead without a blink, bless her brave heart!

"Really! conte," she said. "Well, I was going to say that Alfano is so different from friends of mine at home ——"

At this the Austrian baroness came in sympathetically; romance was her only connection with life.

"You mean your fiancé, dear mademoiselle?"

"Yes, baroness." This time she flushed crimson.

"Now that is too pretty," the baroness cooed. "Do tell us about him. What is he like?"

"He's a big, fine fellow," the girl said, proudly.

"Ah, yes, a beeg fine fellow," the baroness repeated, "now there, *ma chère*, I do not quite understand you. Why is it that American young ladies have told me so often of the beeg fine fellow? With us the beegest men are the porters. It is too droll, but we learn from the animal kingdom that the most intelligent animal is the ant, and he is the smallest. The elephant is the beegest animal, and all the sense he has is to deeg a hole in the ground and put his foot in it."

"But we must not spoil the signorina's dreams!" the conte proffered quickly.

"Oh, you don't at all. I think it's very interesting. You see, I've got used to being in foreign countries."

"And so you wouldn't like an Italian husband?"

"I'm afraid it doesn't sound very polite, conte ——"

The conte made a little, martyr's gesture, as if to say she was not to spare him.

"But I'm afraid I don't think I should. I suppose it's only natural that an American girl should prefer an American husband."

"I know, *cara signorina*, but that does not say that they are superior."

"I'm sure they are, just the same." She was getting a little excited with the argument.

"And why, signorina?"

"Well, for one thing, you know how Italian husbands act. And nobody seems to mind about these affairs, everybody takes it for granted. Our husbands are different, *that* you can certainly say for them. They are not like — I mean you are always hearing in Italy — I mean American husbands are faithful."

"Exactly, *cara signorina*," the conte answered; "of course they are faithful. But what good are they?"

The young lady stretched her honest eyes, but had no answer. She seemed to be floored. She had never thought of this approach to the argument. "Yes, but — I mean —" she murmured, and made a little laugh, and retreated, for the time being, to her cherries.

The baroness began to lisp about a visit she had made that morning to San Domenico — it was too sweet — and the lovely brother there in a black cowl who had given her a rose.

VII

NOTES

I

GIFTS AND ALABASTER

My friend Mrs. W is a little woman of nearly sixty. She is the daughter and the sister of American generals and the divorced wife of a musician; and her forty years' European living and her lifelong cultivation rest on a game foundation. The second year of the war she was suddenly cut off, through conditions in Italy and litigations at home, from her income. She applied to the Red Cross for a position. They sent her to Volterra.

Volterra is a hill town, southwest of Florence, near the sea. It is one of the oldest places in Italy, and belonged for centuries to the Etruscans, that mysterious race that defied so long the power of Rome. The country there is Etruscan still. Peasants on the neighboring farms still turn up the pots of these people. To all appearances their souls lived among those dark stern pots of theirs; they were born in pots, lived in pots, died in pots, and were buried with pots around them. Diggers in the earth often stumble on graves and stone tombs where there are ladies with fierce iron ornaments, and lying amid spearheads and swords are gentlemen seven feet high. On the tops of their sarcophagi are statues of them, stern gentry without blandishment save for the archaic smile which the sculptors did not know how to avoid. By the side of them Rome itself seems soft.

The region around Volterra is entirely volcanic. There are violent rocks thrown out on the mountainsides, and sudden cliffs and declivities everywhere. The grim gray roads wind in and out among lava formations and grave pasture-lands. And here and there at times the earth cracks and makes chasms that swallow up whatever is near.

As you ride, first of all you see the prison castle of the town like a huge ship on the side of the hill. And afterward you enter the gray, fierce, narrow, old streets, with arms of podestàs and iron-studded doors and sudden downward slopes to where the streets end in a cliff, and the far-off, tragic country of mountains and deep

93

valleys appears. And just below one side of
the town there is a place — how shall I say it?
There is a church, there was a church, there will
be a church — for penitent souls. At any rate
there was a church there, there is another now,
and there will still be another, for the ground
has swallowed up one church and now the other
nears the caving rifts.

Sea air and mountain air with their heroic
tang blow over Volterra. The inhabitants carry
their heads high and walk with a kind of fierce
freedom. Their chief occupation is, as it should
be, stone-working. Most of the men who do not
farm the land outside the walls are employed
in the alabaster shops.

My friend arrived in Volterra in the late
autumn with the country grimmer than ever
and the people beginning to go about with their
heads covered from the sharp mountain wind.
She took rooms in a villa outside the gates, not
very far from the church that is to vanish in
the next chasm. The padrona, who owned the
villa and lived in two rooms of it, belonged to
one of the half dozen oldest families in Italy.
She was kind but superstitious, so that Mrs. W,
in addition to having to go around the villa to

enter by the one lucky door, had, among other
charms and omens, to take great care not to de-
velop the evil eye, in the fear of which her host
used to look at her very searchingly from time
to time. However, she settled herself there in an
enormous room with superb furniture and faded
brocades and high ceilings and shadows lurking
everywhere; and rented rooms in an old palace
of the town as Red Cross Headquarters.

But she was not long in finding out that the
Red Cross had a bad name in Volterra. The
committee at Florence had meant well enough,
perhaps, but some one had cheated the givers
in America. It was a fact, at least, that the
first box, already distributed, had been filled
up with worthless goods. The goods had been
worse than worthless, they had been dangerous.
Mrs. W began to hear details.

For example, there were shoes with paper
soles, and the tacks had gone through. And
shoes had been one of the things most needed.
There were skirts made of a soft cottony stuff
like velvet, of dreadful colors and dyes; the
shirts for the men were too small, unless people
were to be strangled. Some of the clothes had
printing on them, big letters in black paint,

which was certain to mean ill luck. Such an
offering was vile and insulting. It was bad
enough to be poor people ruined by the war
and to have to take charity, but to be treated
like dogs! Most of this account Mrs. W got
from the good priest.

"But," she said to the good father, "they are
looking a gift horse in the mouth."

"I know, signora," he said simply, and perhaps without committing himself, "the things
are indeed given to them by the rich Americani.
My people are a little hasty, perhaps, but they
are good people."

More exact details began to come in. The
canton-flannel skirts had all run and faded in the
first wash and had dyed all the sheets and under-
clothes purple and green, and no one could bear
the sight of them. People felt, may God help
us, as if they were going to bed in the meadows
or the slaughter-pens! *Ma che!* The shoes
had come through on the stone roads, even
after the cobbler had hammered down the tacks.
That is why people limped as they did. Four
X's written on a chemise had caused the death
of an old woman's pig. And why did the Americani send six pairs of trousers in which the mea-

sures of the waistbands were so much greater than the length, unless this mistake had been made on purpose and sent there to torture poor people? *Ma che!* In short, Volterra had been insulted. They were only waiting for the next box to show what they were going to do.

Mrs. W had no intention of turning back. She asked the priest again for advice. He said he would speak to the people, but it would be better for the signora to ask the council for some gendarmes.

A big box arrived in due time and was delivered at the Red Cross office. The council sent gendarmes to stand on each side of the entrance. Another gendarme escorted Mrs. W from the villa to the palace. They opened the box and saw with dismay that the assortment of things was the same as the first box. What could Florence mean? Did they choose the poorest things for Volterra or was it an oversight? At any rate the distribution had to go forward. The distribution by the Red Cross of the supplies to the needy citizens of Volterra had been announced in little bills pasted up in the town. People would be coming in from miles around.

The palace where the office was, was set back from the street ten feet or more. There was a wall with a gate; the posts were ornamented with ancient Etruscan urns. The gendarmes left the gate free for the beneficiaries.

After a while Mrs. W heard them coming. There was a long file of people singing and shouting. They piled into the courtyard, the gendarmes keeping them out of the house, and the distribution began from the door.

Volterra had a sense of justice. They waited to see what the new goods were to be like. When they saw the shoes and recognized the skirts and gowns, the riot began. Yells and oaths burst out. They threw the clothing and shoes and skirts into the air and stamped on them with curses and shouts. They smashed the ancient urns on the wall. An old woman was trampled. They broke down the gate. Some people threw shoes into the fountain. They would have sacked the house but for the guards.

Finally, singing and cursing, they went away. And for days, all along the road that led down the hill by the castle, there were hats on the lamp-posts and shoes stuck into the hedges.

The bushes were dressed up in skirts, purple canton flannel many of them. The young trees here and there had nightgowns on them.

Mrs. W kept to the villa for a while. She sent off an account of the sack to Florence and begged them to look carefully at the next box, there had been a terrible mistake. And Volterra was a wild place, not like Tuscany.

Then she went to the priest and guaranteed better goods next time. On this assurance he went about pacifying the people and telling them they had been very wrong to act as they had, it was a great sin. Finally a box of excellent things arrived.

But for three or four weeks Mrs. W went about Volterra with much uneasiness. She took the main streets and kept as much as possible to the middle of the street. As a soldier's daughter, reared in barracks, she meant to see the thing through. And it was not that she was afraid of being killed.

"What I was afraid of all the time," she said, "was that alabaster."

This form of attack, she explained, derives from the chief industry of the town. It is the favorite method of revenge in Volterra,

99

apart from stabbing matters. If you wish to avenge a wrong or to punish an enemy, you take a pail of alabaster dust, fine as the wind almost, into an upper window or a balcony, and wait for him to pass, and throw it down on his head. The alabaster not only ruins the clothing but gets into the eyes, the hair, the nose and throat and lungs, with terrible effect.

II

MODERNISM IN SIENA

My friend Don Paolo — my professor of Italian — is one of the most modern men in Siena. He is a priest, between forty and fifty years old, with gray hair, strong white teeth, and a body as powerful as a boxer's. Don Paolo is pointed out by his friends as one of the three priests in Siena who have not a mistress, a phase of modernity which his enemies profess to doubt wholly, and at any odds a piece of idle chatter. He is not only modern, but modern to such a degree that he is pointed out darkly by many people in Siena as a menace. And every one there knows that *moderno* is his favorite word. *Moderno!*

100

This modernity of Don Paolo's is not a mere recent thing. It was not stirred up by the upheaval of the war. He began long ago by establishing a recreation home for boys in Siena. His idea was primarily to keep the boys off the street and to give them an education in athletics, bathing, and the other interests usually regarded as Boy Scout activities in England and America. He got hold of an old house in his parish, turned the garden into a playground, put in a swimming-pool, tennis-courts, and even built a printing-press and a little theatre. The boys learned to write and act their own plays and to issue under their own pens a little weekly journal. The money for this he got partly by giving lessons in Italian to foreigners and partly from English residents and their friends at home, who were interested in the benefits of such an enterprise for Siena.

On this experiment Siena was very much divided. Many citizens were scandalized. There were many people who said that the archbishop should curb these wild ideas in one of his clergy. It took boys away from home. It sinned against the family. It attempted to destroy the influence of their parents over them. It was irre-

ligious. There were as many who laid it all to
a rank ambition of Don Paolo's for the archbishop's mantle of Siena. Nevertheless, the
experiment succeeded. And every day it is
more secure; for Don Paolo's boys are growing
up and have become citizens of Siena to defend
him. There is a tablet in his garden of those
who fell in the war.

Don Paolo is a power in politics. He is
something of a leader in the Partito Popolare.
He has even had conferences with the Holy
Father in the Vatican, who has counselled pru-
dence. He believes that the land ought to
come back to the contadini who work it. He
does not believe that it should be confiscated
by the state and turned over to the contadini
— that would be socialism or something wrong;
he thinks that an arrangement should be made
by which, in the course of time, they could buy
it with their labors, instead of the present hopeless system by which the landlords have hold
over everything. Not only that, but they are
sitting back and letting an immense exodus go
from the land to the towns and into the indus-
tries, and so ruining the one hope of Italy,
which is that the country be made self-supporting

102

as far as food goes. Don Paolo would not advocate the same scheme for church properties, however. *Ma che!* Rather! That is another matter, my dear friend, he tells me. They belong to no private individual and are not administered for private good, and they should be left where they will be most useful.

Don Paolo believes too in women's rights. He was carried away with delight on the fair day when the suffrage was given to Italian women. And he celebrated the event in his paper when the law was passed giving married women property rights.

"It is mediæval, absurdly mediæval," he said he had long said, "that in Italy a married woman could not draw a check, could not go to the bank in her own name."

And he always declared it equally mediæval that Italian women were legally liable to be locked out if they stayed abroad longer than the time granted them by their husbands. What an outrage on civilization!

He even went so far as to say that women had a right to smoke in the cafés, as they are doing since the war. Was there not the old countess in the Via Ricasoli who for years had put on her furs and leaned out of her palace window smoking a cigar as she watched the crowds pass? Why this special privilege merely because she was of a great family? And why cherish these historical prejudices? Let the dead past bury its dead. Why should the Sienese hate the Florentines as they do? After all it is four hundred years and more since they fought each other. Half of Siena thinks Don Paolo disloyal for that sentiment about Florence.

And in the housing agitation in Siena since the war, Don Paolo has been a firebrand.

"It is an outrage and a disgrace to civilization," he thundered and would thunder whenever the subject came up, "that these great palaces in Siena should be vacant when there are so many poor people without a place to lay their heads." He knew poor families with ten people sleeping in a room.

Of course we all know the misfortunes of Siena, he said, since the houses, for a mile along the east wall especially, had all fallen down after the great plague of 1348. But still, look at the Saracini Palace. A hundred rooms in extent and nobody there but the caretaker, unless Conte Borghese chose to give a concert in the

104

music salon. There were men in Siena who owned three or four palaces besides villas in the country. And look there opposite the post-office at the great palace, whose owner will allow nobody to live in it since her son's death; it stands there furnished from top to bottom and vacant. No wonder we are on the edge of a revolution all the time.

All these ideas Don Paolo speaks of and makes orations about. And he defies the conservatives in Siena, who would like to have him sent off to a retreat in the North, if the archbishop would only do as most people think he would like to do with this Bolshevik.

And Don Paolo edits a weekly paper, which is read at the Socialists' Club and by every sort of wild revolutionary. He has a thundering and eloquent style and is without fear, seemingly. And young hot-heads all over town quote his editorials.

Don Paolo told me that he had not believed in the war. "I am a modern," he said with his eyes blazing, "and war is antiquated. It is mediæval, a mediæval encumbrance on modern civilization."

We used to sit and talk about these matters

during our lesson period. Was there going to be a revolution in Italy? Don Paolo thought not. The Italians had too much common sense; besides, they were too indifferent to principles carried into action. As for the war, Italy had been badgered into it. She was between two fires. She had won the war and lost everything, as everybody in Italy was saying. Often the whole hour passed with the place resounding under his great voice. I had no objection. His flow of faultless Tuscan was better for me than any grammar exercises.

One morning, after Easter, I decided to vary from the socialists and revolutions and turn the talk on a special point in dogma. Don Paolo would give me the explanation in contemporaneous terms.

I had been seeing everywhere in Siena over the church doors the Indulgenza Plenaria. It seemed a difficult doctrine to reconcile with our modern thinking. I asked Don Paolo to explain, then, the idea of Plenary Indulgence, what it meant to a man like him, for I know of course, as I told him, the general doctrine, popularly held.

He would be delighted to tell me, he said.

106

There are some sins, of course, he said, that are easily forgiven. If a man truly repents he can expiate them in this life. Or in a few years in purgatory. But there were some sins which Almighty God could not forgive without a profound expiation on the sinner's part. Say, for instance, a man committed a sin for which he would be given, say, three hundred thousand years in purgatory, that is, before his soul could be cleansed from it. And, seeing the difficulty of this, the church had established a method by which the sinner could expiate at least a portion of this great sin here in this world. Some penance he could do, like a pilgrimage or much prayer or noble work. Or it might be more possible or convenient for many men to give money by way of expiation. A man might build a hospital or help the poor or make a foundation of some sacred kind or give money to the church. Or he might contribute to the support of some order like that at Certosa, each member of which community lived alone in his cell, had his own garden, his food passed in to him, and never spoke except for one meal a week at which all the brothers sat together. These orders represented a living sacrifice for the sins of men. By paying in this way a sinner could at least avoid such a long punishment and perhaps have only fifty thousand years to serve in purgatory instead of four hundred thousand. We must, you see, have every means we can invent to fight the power of the devil.

"Ah, yes," I said, seeing our plight and trying to escape. "And must one believe in the devil exactly?" I asked. "Or may I think of him, of it, as a state in which, for the time, our less good qualities are in the majority?"

"Not at all, oh, no," he said, with the same look in his eye as when he talked about the landlords in Siena. "He is a being. Rather! The devil is a fallen angel. He is an evil spirit. The devil is God's opponent. We must fight him!"

III

THE SHRINE

From where I stand I can see him coming down the path from the fields above. On one hand he has the stream bank that follows the slight line of the water, in this season of summer almost dry; and on the other, planted among the olive-trees, the wheat, now yellow toward the

108

harvest. At the bottom of the slope the stream circles into a pool, with green poplars beyond and trees with young pears, and the tiles, half hidden, of the farmhouse roof. Another path borders the fields where the land stretches out into a long level with vines and the elms they hang upon, and wheat again, filled thick with poppies. At the crossing of the paths stands a shrine, a square pillar plastered white. A little roof of tiles covers the top of the shrine and not far down is a niche, painted blue with gold stars. In it is a little statue of the Virgin, white and blue, with stars about her head.

The sun has sunk, the late golden light fills the air and sifts through the olive-trees and gleams on the white shrine. The bells from San Francesco far away in Assisi come down over the serene land. Sounds can be heard now from the kitchen of the farmhouse, and presently a woman begins to sing, in a stone room; you can tell by a kind of completeness of volume in the tone. Her voice has an odd double quality, something of the sweetness of light and the tang of metal.

The man is tall and brown; he is young, not yet thirty. Three-quarters of the way to the foot of the slope he stops and turns and looks back up the hill. Then he turns again and stands looking for a long time out over the fields. Then he goes back and breaks a white-flowered branch from an olive-tree and a handful of poppies growing underneath, and comes and lays them at the shrine.

The light, the olive boughs, the wheat, the abundance and verdure are reflected within him as they are in the water of the pool. Love and thankfulness fill his heart. But he is not abstract; and it would not satisfy him, even if he could, to hold in some memory or system of thought or state of mind what he feels. He needs some one to offer it to; and he needs to do some visible act that he can see as a result of the thing in him. And in what he does, the labor, the plenty, the rest and peace, reach their completeness and fruition and are made clear; his day takes its natural place in the world. For him the idea and the body or creation appear as one, in the same way as that in which the progress and life in nature there around him may relieve and express itself in the ripening grain, the flowers, the fruit, and the evening light under the trees.

IV

THE TEXAN

He grew up on a ranch somewhere north of San Antonio. But a year ago an oil-well came in on the land, and his father, being well enough off now to afford it easily, sent him abroad for a year to travel. And so he turns up here in Assisi, this little town of St. Francis in the Umbrian hills.

He had had two sessions at some college in his State, he tells me, but most of his twenty-three years had been spent on the ranch, where his special business was with the cattle on the ranges. At some seasons of the year he had been a long way from the ranch-house, most of the time alone. Sometimes for three months he saw no one except the boy who came once a week with supplies and spent the night and went home again next morning. He had read some four or five Shakespeare plays for one thing, he remembered, and some books he found lying around the house; but most of the time he spent riding the range on his horse; or looking after cattle that strayed up the little canyon there was there; or often just sitting around, as

111

he called it. His camp was by a stream where there was a clump of trees; all the rest of the country was bare as far as you could see and spotted with brush; and there was a narrow pool where he could take a plunge. He cooked, and took care of himself. There were a great many birds that settled in the trees and always at night you could hear the coyotes in the brush.

He likes Assisi. He has read little or nothing about it except what is in the guide-book, but he feels at home in Assisi, which is a way of understanding it. Without knowing much about the various periods of art in the upper and lower churches, he goes there again and again. He comes in from the narrow, high old streets with a clear look in his gray eyes. I see him down below the south gate walking along the path under the olive-trees beside the stream. Twice at night I have run on him standing in the piazza by the lower church looking up that steep, incredible stair that seems to lead into the deep sky. And in his room he has got now a little framed picture of St. Francis. He says nothing of any of this. Day after day he says he must go soon, but he stays on.

V

CAMPO SANTO

I come into the Campo Santo by the only entrance in those four walls and into the shadow of the roof that rests one side on them and the other on those lines of slender columns that enclose the court. The columns begin high up from the pavement, five feet or more, standing on a solid wall that runs all around, with openings for passageways in the centre of each side and of the ends. Down the long gallery that the high outer walls and the lower wall around the court make, I walk; and from there I look up at the columns rising gray and slender against the light, I see the line of a cypress and a stretch of blue sky; on the far side of the court the columns' white marble shines in the light, and they define themselves against the shadow beyond, with its glow of frescoes and old sculptures. There are four cypresses within the court and in the centre an altar with yellow roses climbing around it. In the air above, against the blue of the sky, white pigeons are flying. And now and then a sound from Pisa comes faintly and almost lost, and the crackle

113

and darting rustle of the tiny life in the grasses and plants near by. But that more subtle silence of the eyes lies everywhere.

There is nothing else; only the long galleries of shade with their walls painted over in crucifixions and Calvary, the damnations of hell and the pageantries of life, now faded into ghosts; and beneath the frescoes the tombs, of Roman and mediæval and later times, the tablets, busts, and sepulchral monuments, and the eternal memory of them; the slender white columns beginning so far from the ground and running up to the marble fretwork within the arches; the light; the cypress-trees; the white pigeons flying; the blue of the sky; the quiet.

On the steps leading down into the court a man and a woman are reading in English a guide-book. The earth in this plot was brought here from Palestine in fifty-three shiploads by the Crusaders in 1203. The man and the woman close the guide-book and go on talking about the legend of this place. They speak to each other at length of the sentiment of all this, and then of superstition. But even if the earth here had not been brought from the Holy Land, they say, it would have made no difference to speak of,

114

since the spot had been blessed by the church, as all cemeteries must be. It would be for Catholic Italians a special and sacred place; the superstition would remain the same. They marvel at the force of superstition among men.

But — however one may think of other cemeteries blessed by priests and specially revered — what has happened here in the Campo Santo is the reverse of all superstition, which is the act of giving to a thing a worship or fear or belief that has no longer any reason to exist or that is arbitrarily superimposed upon it. A savage may bring offerings to a malicious rock or bow to some crossroads as ill-omened or beneficent. But here the Campo Santo has not been left a mere accidental plot of ground superstitiously endowed with powers. The beauty, quietness, and grave repose, the even balance and finality and immortal hope believed of it have become its visible and tangible aspect. Through its marbles and color, its spaces, its sharp-ending clear lines, its light falling through shadow, the ideas held about this burial spot have attained a material actuality. The men who believed that this was a special and sacred place have saved their minds and ours from the insult of

115

superstition by putting into it what was special and sacred out of themselves and making it the substance of their faith; as a man might who, worshipping music as his own inmost voice, made his inmost voice into a music. This is the salvation and health of all inner life, when it attains an outer and separable expression of itself in words or color, line and form, or sound or action. The sanity and wholeness of all things is saved only by bringing them to their due ends or fruits in the world. And believers are not ignorant merely in thinking this Campo Santo to be divine and holy and in setting it apart; in so far as there is any divinity in their thought or holiness in their souls, these have been re-created here in form and light and have become the place.

VI

SMOKE

Over toward Montefiascone a smoke rises from a pine wood in the hills. Above the darker spot of the pines and up against the purple of the hills in the morning light, the smoke rises in a thin white line. It might well come from

on their heels about the decks. And best of all was one old peasant woman, long past seventy, from somewhere in Asia Minor, who sat lolling against a bale of luggage made from a Turkish rug and laced about with cords. There was something very bonny and blithe about her — the little brown face, wrinkled like a walnut-shell, the bright black eyes, the white teeth, the finger-tips stained red with henna; her chatter never leaving off, and the young soldiers gathering about her, talking, listening, laughing, and lighting for her the cigarettes which they presented and which she smoked one after another as she reclined there, holding them airily in her hand and making gestures with them as she talked. I stood watching her and the young soldiers. And as I watched I could hear the sound of the pipe, the far-off concertina, the rich voices, the laughter, the shuffling feet, the songs here and there, against the low flap of the sails, and the wind in the rigging and the long murmuring swish of the blue water alongside.

Meanwhile Athens faded in the soft light, sunset came on and passed; the gleaming Acropolis, with Pentelicon beyond and Lykabettos

and the other mountains there, grew more and
more like a dream. The pipe left off; and the
old man who played it, seeing me watching him
perhaps, came over to me smiling and said in
broken Italian that he could write his name, if
the signore would allow him; and spelt out for
me on an envelope *Sophocles Anastasiou*. There
it was, he said. And then in the golden light
we saw the temples of Corinth, high up to the
south of the canal, bright on the barren, tawny
hilltop, the wretched modern town below almost
forgotten in the lengthening shadows. The
temples arose in that strange poetry that
columns take with their lines against the air;
they seemed far away, ageless, beautiful, solitary. There was no longer any wind and the
sails had grown quieter; the water and the sails
made only one low sound.

I heard a voice behind me.

"Well," it was saying, "I don't wonder St.
Paul wrote to the Corinthians."

I recognized the nasal twang of him and
turned to listen. A man in tweeds stood there
beside a lady in tweeds, just behind me. He
was pointing up toward that high summit of
old Corinth, which seemed higher than ever in

the fading light, and he repeated his joke with more stress.

"No, sir; I don't wonder St. Paul *wrote* to the Corinthians. It's what I'd 'a' done."

I nodded and tried to smile agreeably; after all there must have been worse jokes from travellers in Greece. He shook hands.

"So you are from the States?" he said. "Meet my wife." And then, as I was about to introduce myself, he started and caught at his wife's arm, and snapped his fingers.

"*By George!*" he said. "By George!"

"What?" I asked, for this was startling. "What is it?"

"Nothing. *By George!* Say!" He turned on his wife. "Have you got it? Did you see what I did with it? Say ——!"

"Oh, dear!" she cried; and they began tracing themselves about the harbor, to the fruit-shop, the postal cards, the restaurant near the quay. I offered to help them. Could I help them? I asked. Was there anything I could do?

There was not, they answered; nothing could be done. I must pardon them. They had forgotten something, that was all, the lady said; they had left something.

"A piece of an antique statue," the man said; "piece of an antique statue."

An antique statue! I was very sorry. I asked about it; where they had found it; how they were getting it out of Greece, through the customs. Was it large? It was only a small thing, they replied. And from their details I concluded that they knew nothing of marbles.

Forget it, they said. We forgot the antique, therefore, and passed to other subjects. He was from Brown University, he told me, and had been three years in a missionary college somewhere near Constantinople. A stocky man, under thirty, with stiff thick hair, a short nose, strong teeth and hands, and honest gray eyes, he seemed very boyish and innocent and hearty and simple as he stood there talking with that honest staccato of his and in that careless voice. His wife was a big, athletic young woman — she was from Mount Holyoke College, he said — with a broad, honest face also, thick braids, bright color, handsome in her way like a great oatmeal loaf, full of serious health and moral intention, piously romantic too, though a trifle heavy and dull. We talked, and I inquired

122

about their lives there in the East, if they had
felt its power, if they had known many Turks,
if they meant to return. No, they had seemed
rather to be back at home in America in many
ways, staying there at the college with the work,
the teaching, and the personal contacts; so much
could be done in the work by personal contact.
They had had a delightful circle at the college
and often very pleasant evenings together,
everybody; or writing letters home. But they
were, of course, very glad to get back again to
God's country after so long. Now they were
going to tour Italy on their way north; they had
been saving up money for that. That's why
they were coming steerage, to save for Italy.
Did I know some good hotels not too dear? I
named hotels and said that on this boat the
steerage was more interesting, no doubt; on
the upper deck there were largely tourists and
business agents. They said that after all it
was only one night and they liked to sleep out,
fine nights now. After a while I wandered off to
another part of the ship. "Perhaps your marble
will turn up somewhere in your things," I said
consolingly as I left.

"No hope of that," the young man said; "fat

chance we got!" I admired his stoical endurance.

Off Patras there was some sort of delay, two days of quarantine for a fever on board; and I had a chance to see more of the passengers. The most interesting figure among them, among the sixty or more tourists and agents in the first cabin, was a young American, a fellow of twenty, not very tall, with a pallid, yellowish, ivorylike skin, large, vague gray eyes, and loose, thick, wide lips. He belonged, evidently, to a party made up otherwise, except for himself and two old ladies, of college girls, under the guidance of a minister; but I never saw him with them. He used to roam about the deck with a note-book in his hand, but seemed shy and spoke to no one. But there was an air about him of some intense centre of living within himself; he had a kind of misty distinction that set him apart from every one on board. I used to wonder what he could be thinking about, and if he was a genius or only a dreamer lost in himself. There was that loose, red, full mouth, there were those brooding gray eyes with their shadows upon that pale quiet face and its cloud of brown hair. I wondered about him. I saw him around the decks, and wondered what things they were that plunged him into such caverns of lonely thought. But he never cared to speak. And then the last night out, as we neared Brindisi, I came upon him in the smoking-room, in a corner, with a glass of Marsala in front of him and his note-book open. I sat down at one side of the table. There was no easy escape for him.

We were getting in before long, I said to him. Too bad; I had hoped he and I might have a talk.

It was two hours yet and more, he said, looking down at his glass. He had wanted to talk with me, too, but he had been afraid of me.

We laughed over that, and began. In five minutes he had become voluble. He was from Salem; he was going to Harvard next year, where he would be a freshman; he was going to do well — he knew that because he knew what he was going there for; so many men went there with nothing really planned and wasted their time. They were not serious in their thoughts.

But the note-book, I asked; was he studying here in this part of the world?

No, no, he said; but of course being in Jerusalem had been very interesting to him because it

125

concerned a subject very interesting to him.
Something he had been studying on and thinking about a long time, for five years. And
what was that? I asked.

"The Resurrection of Christ."

"What about that?"

"Well," he said, "I can prove conclusively
that the account given in the Bible of the Resurrection is not true; it cannot possibly be true."

"Really?" I said, wondering.

"Absolutely." He pushed the glass and the
note-book away from him and brought his palm
down on the table. "Absolutely, and I can
prove it to you. It's this way." He squared
himself against the wall behind him. "The
Bible says explicitly that Jesus was put to death
on the day of the preparation, the day before
their Sabbath, which was Saturday, so that
makes it Friday. Doesn't it?"

I agreed to that.

"Friday. Granted. But mark this! Now,
we know for a fact that the Jewish Sabbath
began on Friday. Friday evening at six o'clock,
to be exact. Granted. There was no time,
then, for preparations for the burial of the body,
since the Jews would do no more than they

could help on the Sabbath. So they had to
get some friend to lend his tomb to be used
temporarily. That must have been the case.
And who was that friend? Joseph of Arimathea.
Now another thing! The Bible says the Marys
stood watching from afar. The cemetery must
have been a very large place; you know how
they were cut into the rock, how one finds them
now in these countries. I was interested to
verify that from personal experience. Well, in
this place there must have been a great number
of these sepulchres or grave openings. How
then could the Marys have seen in just which
tomb the burial took place? And there you
are!"

I remembered the beautiful account in St.
Mark of how the Marys stood watching from
afar that dying figure lifted on the Cross; and
how they were near when Joseph of Arimathea
laid Jesus away in that new sepulchre in a
garden. But it seemed useless to stop this
strange argument or to break the thread that
the young man was weaving so eagerly. I said
only, "Go on."

"Watching from afar," he went on. "Granted.
Well, then, when they came again, bringing

127

frankincense and offerings, how could they in all that number of tombs know which was the one they sought? There must have been, as we have seen, a great many of them, say twelve hundred at least. To be conservative, say twelve hundred or even a thousand tombs. The Marys had stood, say, a quarter of a mile away. Well, what must we conclude? They could not possibly have been able to find the right tomb. They had to ask some one, a caretaker perhaps, or some one's relative there looking around, who told them that He whom they sought was not there. They evidently thought the person was an angel, which was natural enough in their excitement. It frequently happens."

"What frequently happens?" I inquired.

"That people think things when they are excited. Don't you grant that? I can prove it to you."

"Certainly," I said.

"And so this proves that the account of the Resurrection cannot be true. And I've read every commentary on the subject. I've thought about it for years. I've always been interested in religion, had ancestors that were, in Salem and other places. I know all the arguments. But they won't stand. Every Sunday when I'm in church I think of this and have all I can do not to get up and debate with the minister. But if I did that, my old man would die, and grandmother would — my mother's not living, she died when I was a child. He's a family friend, that's why I'm on this tour with him. But I could prove it to him."

His eyes were blazing. The pale brow was flushed, a vein stood out; I could see its throbbing. I tried to shift the subject a little, by teasing him on his consistency.

"But then, in this case," I said, "if you believe as you do about the Resurrection and discard all that part of the Bible as you do, how can you consider yourself a Christian and go to church?"

"I don't know. Like the form of it, I suppose. It's a good place to sit and think. And I like music."

"But if you feel that your argument is so important, I should think you would have to stand by your convictions."

"Habit, I guess," he said.

"Well," I said, "it's very hard to understand how you can combine all this."

He shrugged his shoulders, and I added teasingly, and trying to make the point fantastically, which after all seemed the kindest way out:

"Suppose you firmly believed that we should all have our teeth pulled out. Had proved this completely to yourself. And yet you went on keeping your teeth in because the people around you believed in having teeth ——"

But his eyes lit up again. He brought his fist down with a bang on the table ——

"Take the modern teeth," he burst out; "what are they? Are they any good? Are they not degenerating steadily? How many people, tell me, do you see with good, sound teeth? Not these days. And yet we all know how much the health depends on having good teeth, don't we?"

It seemed too much to believe. I was overwhelmed, and began to howl with laughter. But the young man was going on, sitting straight up, making points against hot breads, hot drinks, modern nerves, tooth brushes, modern haste. Ten minutes at least had passed before he was interrupted by the professor from the missionary college, who came rushing into the room and up

130

to me. He was unshorn and battered, for the three days instead of the one expected in the steerage had been hard on him.

"I've been looking for you all over the place," he said. "Look, we're about to land. See the light out there? The houses? Brindisi. Wanted to say good-by. My wife asked me to say good-by for her too. We're off for Rome."

The Salem youth had hurried away to find his party, and the two of us left now went outside on the deck.

But it was so late, signori, they were explaining to the passengers, that after all we could not land and must lie at anchor till the port officials came down in the morning and admitted us.

And I stood there resting my elbows on the rail and thinking how this was the ancient harbor of the stag's head, the Brentesion of the Greeks, the Brundisium of the Romans, whose Appian Way led down to it; Brundisium, where the embarkations for the East were made, where Pompey withstood Cæsar for so long a siege, where St. Paul landed, and Virgil died, and a thousand years later the Crusaders gathered. The quays were deserted now, save for a group of workmen and, in the shadow of a pile of

131

shipping, an old man and a boy, squatting on their heels. It was a breathless summer night; the white houses and piazzas of the town lay scattered in gleaming squares and spaces of black shadows, the squares of white dropping away and growing smaller and whiter as they went into the low hills of the country round. There were lights in the taverns along down the water-front, from the Hotel International, from a house now and then over the town, and now and then a street lamp, but very few. In a garden here and there black cypresses stood up; I could see the faint motion of them in the low wind, on which the smell of wine lees drifted to me. And then the old man, when he learned that there were passengers stirring on the deck, rose and came forward to the edge of the water, leaning on a staff and the boy leading him, and began to sing.

O bella Rosalia, la mia fanciulla!

he sang, standing on the stones that at this hour were silent and so white in the summer moon-light, sweeping his guitar and calling some mad passion that he knew into his faded voice. A sailor down near the prow began to sing also,

132

the same song, and the crowd there to curse at him and laugh and applaud, and the two voices rose with a strange, solitary brightness together. The sea had grown stiller than the white town. And I was carried into that silence and space and eternity; and I was lost in them as they in me. Time and the world seemed about me everywhere; and through them the water, the light, the silence, and the wind seemed to pass.

My companion leaned over toward me and shook my hand.

"Look," he said, "good-by. And what I really want to say is that there wasn't any antique statue about it. What we left behind was a cold chicken. A cold roast chicken we had brought from Olympia for lunch on board, see? Don't want to be telling you a lie."

IX

TWO WALKS

It was the beginning of June when I came to Tivoli. Around the town with the gray, dark stone of its houses and streets spread the yellow country of the harvest. It stretched away over the plains, past Hadrian's villa, toward the Campagna and Rome and the hills beyond. Only here and there rose the black points of cypresses and clumps of ilex and the verdure winding sometimes along beside a stream. It was a wide, clear world of light, a golden expanse from which the hill arose, with its woods and their cataracts, and the gray town, with the Cardinal d'Este's villa on one side the slope.

In my mind, as I went along on my way to the Villa d'Este, I carried the utmost idea of romantic gardens, of sombre and splendid avenues of trees and ancient marbles and now and then a ruined fountain; a dream of past splendor and half-forgotten courts. In my mind's eye I had that picture that one sees everywhere in houses and in shops, of the stone table with the two benches and, stretching away behind them, an aisle with dark cypresses on either side. But the truth was I was translating these qualities into my own conceptions of them; and now, when I arrived at the villa, the translation of my romantic and sombrely poetic idea back again into these Italian meanings was to be sudden and illuminating. For in that light of afternoon the first thing that shot across my mind when I saw the d'Este garden was how much less obviously romantic it was than I had thought. The table and the benches were near the villa itself; the wide paved promenade ran in front of the windows and led by stairs here and there to lower levels, where the cypress walk began. And this walk was neither very romantically long nor mysterious. The d'Este garden was romantic, it had its mystery and possibility, but not in the sense that I had thought. It was more open, more supported by idea. It was more mechanically formal, more arranged, more of this world.

And yet in the end, after all, one may set down only the mood of this place. Form is impossible to describe, it alone can describe itself; and half the d'Este garden is formal art.

135

What those varying planes and levels are cannot be expressed; nor the nuances of the diverse heights to which the trees and plantations ascend; nor those stairs leading up and down, those patterns of walks and hedges, those arbors, that rondel of cypresses around a basin of water, those sudden oncomings where vistas lead out from the garden lines to the country that spreads away in a shining and soft transparency of summer air. The abstraction of pure form underlies this garden. The lines of natural things and of paths and plots of flowers and earth and shapes of water are made to compose a pattern beyond themselves, something independent of them, a luminous geometry of pure idea. Abstract design underlies this garden as it does great music or painting.

In this garden there were trees; there was infinite water coming down from the hillside above and led everywhere to a hundred jets and falls. There were rococo caverns with statues of deities, baroque gods and goddesses whose grottoes were filled with green shadows and streams and cascades and the drip and splash and rumor of unending water. There were pseudo ruins in stone and rococo antiquities.

136

I saw a statue lying in two parts, as if despoiled
by centuries, half buried in the ground. I saw
the Diana of the Ephesians, colossal in sand-
stone, with the hundred breasts that nourished
the world. At the end of a fading flight of
steps, as if some acropolis had to be reached
there, I saw the miniature conceit of an ancient
classical city, scattered on a little terrace,
temples, theatres, and monuments done in stone
and cement. I could hear at every step some
unseen splashing of water and a steady murmur
of streams of water falling in the cascades, the
fountains, and the tiny cataracts in the grottoes
of those ornamental and redundant deities.
The water of these was invisible, but on the
aspect of the things in the garden lay its fantasy
and sweetness. I came again and again to see
that famous stairway that all artists sketch
but none ever expresses, with its great jet of
water rising into the air, its ivy, its two flights
of steps and their balustrade, descending with
such gracious and incredible suavity and beauty
to the terrace below. Three square pools,
raised two feet and more from the ground,
stretched in a line parallel with the villa's
façade; they were lifted like mirrors above the

level of the walks, and above them the boughs
of the ilex-trees hung down and lightly touched
the water. The d'Este garden was first of all
a majestic, sophisticated place done by a knowing hand. It was first grave and then ornate.
The mind behind this art was beautiful; it was
tragic; it was mature with a passion of knowledge
and rich choice.

For hours I walked, through lanes of ilex and
laurel, and paths that led through copses and
thickets smelling of pine and bay and oleanders,
and down avenues of cypress-trees. I seemed
to be in the midst of a living silence. There
was in the garden a kind of vivacity of quiet.
Over by the wall nearest the town a group of
workmen with a mandolin were laughing and
talking and breaking out now and then into
snatches of songs. A long plane of late golden
light crept under the lowest boughs of the trees.
The late twilight was drawing on.

As the light grew less and less a completeness
came over the d'Este garden around me. Now
that the details of the grounds faded and the
surrounding country and sky receded and grew
dim, the garden seemed more to be one thing,
the larger masses gathered all into themselves,

138

the order and design of the place stood out.
Night came on and gradual darkness. There
was no moon but an early starlight showed above
the trees and through the vistas opening out
beneath. In the darkness the glint of the walks
appeared and the lines of the balustrades. The
unstirred surface of the raised pools was like
dim glass. A low wind stirred the long shapes
of the cypresses, and in the laurels and oleanders
made a hushed rustling. In the heavy shade of
the ilexes the nightingales were singing. And
from everywhere, among the leaves and through
the avenues and paths, there came the eternal
sound of water.

The quality of this place was mournful and
rich and elegiac. It satisfied that tragic beauty
that is the soul of the mind. The involved and
extravagant elegance of this garden and its
design, and the eloquence of its use of the
natural resources of water and verdure and light
and earth, were touched with the languor of a
culture that has grown old. The luxury of this
beauty was haunted with an old knowledge of
the end of things. The garden of the Villa
d'Este was warm and intellectual, remote and
passionate. It was like a dark and grandiose

and poignant music rising up, and more poignant because of the elaborate despair of its art and because of its wistful magnificence.

And then that night, some hours later, when I was sitting in my room at the hotel another picture arose in my mind. Coming after the Villa d'Este it was like the thought of a simple and very single melody in the midst of an orchestra. I could see that line of trees near by the stream, that stretch of English green, that quiet, that aspect of peace, Addison's Walk. On the fine old trunks of the trees, the verdant spaces, the trodden path, as I saw them now, the lights and shadows were not very clearly defined, the tone of them was mild and faint. I thought of Addison's Walk with the gentle morning on it, the soft gray perhaps, the English thing. And did we like it after all, I wondered, better than this garden of that sixteenth century Italian, the Cardinal Ippolito d'Este? Did it not steal further and more gently into the heart and the affections? There are many people of English blood who would tell you that it did.

How pleasant it would be, I thought, to fall back on such a preference! The quality of that English scene was sweet and familiar, it was

140

gentle and beloved of me. A man might run back to the memory of it as a child runs to its mother's knee when the wind, the sun, the noise and light and sound and fire of the world becomes too great for him. And yet I knew that all this proved nothing. I could not make my escape by so easy a position. This English scene could give me no more, really, than I might get from things that obviously had nothing to do with art at all. What it could give me I had had once when I came to England after a long stay in Sicily and heard at Folkestone in the dusk of the evening the children's voices speaking our English tongue. I had had this tremor of love and pleasure when I heard across the street in an old town a wretched village choir singing execrable hymns in a vulgar church. I had even had it from Mr. Raphael Tuck's Christmas cards, the kind of card where there is a cross within the frame of which are pictured green pastures and sheep, and around which cluster white narcissus and forget-me-nots; all worse than the Christmas cards of the British royal family, all very Victorian, silly, and soft and bad, but dear to me with an old, sweet memory of childhood and scrap-books. And that kind of association, as I knew very well, that reminder of something gently remembered and loved, was what must remain the only source of appeal of much English art. But what had that to do with a discussion of the d'Este garden and Addison's Walk as art, as creations that express human experience?

Addison's Walk, I sat there that night thinking, was complete and good enough in itself. But art, as Plato said, is the name signifying every cause whereby anything proceeds from that which is not into that which is. Art is a translation by which the material is stated in terms of something else, and something is added which was not there before. Art is a process by which we express one part of our experience, of our contact with the universe, through the medium of another part, adding to it in the process an element of life that was not there before. Addison's Walk, then, like so many English gardens, is scarcely art at all. It is admirable as nature, if you like. As nature it makes quite another discussion. And it exercises one's taste in accidental landscape. But that, too, is another matter.

The garden of the Villa d'Este commits

human nature to a full expression. It takes
the natural world and uses it to express an idea.
Like a painter with his colors, it uses the resources of the earth out of which it creates. It
deals with space and with light, with contrasting
stone and earth, with straight lines and curves,
with varying levels and rhythms of ascent and
descent. It arranges, it takes into account
the stars shining down, the sunlight, the surface
of water, and the boughs above their shadows.
It runs the gamut of visual form, of intellectual
conceit in pattern and design, and of a mystery
of spirit. In it nature and art together are
translated into one complete art. It is a garden
and not nature. It is the mind and the spirit,
the idea and the mood, in terms of out-of-doors.
And that you prefer the Addison's Walk to it
may mean several things. It may mean that
you have little depth and range of life in you to
be expressed and so have no need of any complex
and profound art to express it. It may mean
that your life is deep and rich but incapable of
any consummation in forms of any kind. Or it
may mean that you have a deep and rich life but
have never learned to read the dialect of art,
or at least of this art of gardens, and so do not

look there for the expression of your life or understand what is there expressed. You may like what you choose, but the test of a thing as art does not depend on what you bring to it. It depends rather on the extent to which this thing expresses with power and beauty the dept and complexity of life.

And then suddenly as I sat there letting these thoughts take their will with me, an appalling recollection sprang to my brain. In Siena once we were speaking of poetry, and a lady, a *dottoressa*, very much read in European letters, said to me:

"I am a devotee of your poetry, signor. I read English poetry to rest me."

"To rest you?" I said. "To rest you?"

"After our literature English poetry is so simple. How very direct the mind there is! It is not complicated like ours. There is so little analysis. It is like a child. I read it to rest me."

How well I remembered that remark! It had been one of those things that knock the walls down about your ears.

For, by one of those foolish generalizations that races like to make about one another, I had gone on thinking that there was to the mind in Italian poetry a certain vivid and direct power. It achieved certain large outlines. I had believed, as most English peoples believe, that fortune had reserved for our English poetry the power to probe the last reaches and shadows in the soul; to move deeply and quietly through the depths of experience. I had thought of Italian poetry as something of a refuge from the troubling of the Anglo-Saxon conscience, from the details of our meditations and quiet ways. I had even spoken of the large and vivid simplicity of Italian.

But when the *dottoressa* made her remark I knew at once that I had never really thought all this. I had, at least unconsciously, known all along that such theories of simplicity could not apply to Italian poetry; from the other arts I knew it, if not from poetry. The constant analysis, the energy of mind, the subtle insight and abundant invention of the Italian make-up I had always known. And what I had imagined myself thinking so superficially about Italian poetry were the mere left-overs from impressions of Sicilian acting and from the eyes of a tourist before he learns the language or the country.

145

But even in such a change in my opinion of Italian poetry there was nothing to keep English poetry from being deeper than any other. And to be told by an Italian that she read English poetry for a rest was a shock.

Addison's Walk was not of course so elaborate as many English gardens, but in a simpler way its characteristic excellence was the same as theirs. What then, I thought, if there should be the same difference between English and Italian poetry as there was between the Cardinal's walk and Addison's. In music our ears tell us that we have nothing so great as a score of Continentals. In painting our eyes know that we have no Titian or El Greco or Botticelli or Velasquez. In architecture we have no Michelangelo. But in poetry we have always felt that we were of the modern races supreme. We have liked Dante and Tasso and others, but we have been sure that our English poetry was above all. We have even had a way of saying that the French had no really great poetry, strictly speaking!

I sat there thinking, defensively. Poetry after all is an invisible art. Its medium is words, mere symbols of sense and sound that

146

in themselves are nothing. And how much does the judgment of poetry depend on what one thinks, or one's race or one's generation thinks, to be the nature of the poetic! There can be no doubt, surely, that with us during the last century the idea of the poetic has moved very much away from form and away from a shining and controlling mentality. The average Anglo-Saxon likes to think of poetry as inundated by feeling. He is unduly impressed and led on by certain mere nouns, by mere mentions of infinity, implications of eternity, soul, and other more or less indeterminate and vague, though dear, conceptions. He has associated the poetic with the chaotic, the individual, and the spontaneous. He thinks the subject of poetry must never be mere thoughts or mere arrangements of those radiances that the mind gives off, but almost entirely one's feelings about nature, virtue, love, God, or rebellion. But what if we should come to think otherwise? What if we came to think that poetic quality might arise from a fine order, a profound poise, a subtlety that comes not of suggestions of the unknown or the infinite, but of combinations of exact expressions of thought and renderings of experience? What if, in sum,

147

we came to think of poetry as a social and radiantly definite and communicable art as well as a beautiful spiritual solitude?

Fortunately, I reflected, the matter cannot be settled. Music and pictures pass easily from country to country; neither the medium nor the language is in any way local. Poetry is more untranslatable into another race and country. Dante I knew somewhat, and I knew that he had a kind of vividness, something concrete and poignant, a penetration of the image with the emotion and idea, that is like nothing in our poetry. Leopardi's style rises to a white, marble-like openness and perfection that in English is impossible. And I knew Carducci D'Annunzio with his hot and cold, and Pascoli and something of the Quattrocento. But what were such fragmentary raids when it comes to knowing Italian poetry? And we shall never know Italian poetry, for it has a different language from ours and a different life.

On the other hand, there was Shelley with a quality that could never be in Italian; the very accent of that tongue is against it. He has at his best, when he is not foolish and loose, an ethereal, shimmering world, a translucent and

148

majestic and aspiring beauty. Wordsworth has his revelation of man in the natural world. Spenser, for all his inability to get a unity and a larger pattern into his work and thought, has a marvellous abundance of resource and an intricate and prophetic music to the very top of the English language. What poet anywhere has so diaphanous and so tireless a realm of forms and ideas? And last of all, there was Shakespeare in the sonnets, like all the Renaissance, I knew, but beyond them, I liked to believe, in profundity and character and diffused passion of mind and body. And in "Othello" Shakespeare has the ordered intelligence and elaboration, if you look for that; and in "Macbeth" an ancient, primitive terror, a morality out of the earth, the dreams of kings from desolate and haunted moors, a shudder at once more tragic and more cerebral than in any literature.

And meanwhile always behind my thoughts the d'Este garden moved and the fountains there, and the music of those fountains, too, of light and water and life, from which so much of Italy derives, and of all beauty everywhere.

Neither does it follow, I reflected, consolingly, that because a race has a gift for one art it has

the same amount of capacity for all. The
Italian painting may be better than the English.
Their music may be infinitely superior. But
that need not prove that their poetry is superior
to ours. And the truth may very well be that
poetry is the art most apt to express our Northern race. It may be that in this invisible art
of poetry the hidden force and impact and delicate dreams of our life can most completely
express themselves. Perhaps poetry is the art
most able to express our diffused passion and
tenderness. Perhaps the greatness of Italian
living is best said in painting or acting or music
or cities; and the greatness of Anglo-Saxon living
is best said in poetry. And perhaps not. What
if after all, I asked myself, it should be true that
the art of poetry in Italy and that in England
should be like those two walks? What if, in
this unseen region that poetry is of our own
selves and of the Italians, we jump too easily
at superior conclusions? What if we have as-
sumed too much? I wondered.

X

LOST STARS

In Michelangelo's chapel one March day I was looking at the Pensieroso and thinking what a terrible intensity of living and of spiritual passion was there expressed beneath the poise and sophistication of that figure, what a brooding mystery of shadow was on those eyelids against the delicate finish and distinction of that face. I noted the suave elegance of the surface, and how the slight affectation, and even pedantry, of this statue was spiritualized by the inner violence and force of the artist. I looked at this statue and thought how beautiful and dangerous the life there was.

In the midst of these thoughts I turned suddenly and became aware of a lady sitting in the middle of the room. She was dressed in gray with a cherry color here and there on it; her eyes and her hair gave the impression of a dark violet; and there was a beautiful clear melancholy about her face. I knew at once that she was English by the expression; by the figure,

which was slimmer than that of the Continental
women; and by the bit of ruching which she
wore at her throat and which was just enough
to rout the French perfection of her gown and
leave it persistently her own, with her own elegance and will, rather than the dressmaker's.
She sat there in one of those low Savonarola
chairs, looking up quietly at the statue of the
Medici with his elegant, intense body and the
shadow over his eyes.

Behind this woman's chair a man stood, a
ruddy, athletic Englishman in tweeds, very
smart and very carelessly correct all over, a retired army man I should have said from a first
glance at him. His manner, when there was any,
toward the lady had the air of protecting her —
that was about all. He looked less at the Medici
than she did and more around and up and down
the chapel. Presently I left the two of them
there like that and forgot them.

The first week of April I went down to Assisi
for the coming of spring.

Assisi is one of those hill towns in Italy built
all of stone. It sits there on the top of the hill,
brown and pale rose and ivory color. The stone
houses come down sharp against the stone of the

street; and the whole of the town is dry and ancient and quiet; though so small and wayward as it climbs about, and so gentle with the memories of St. Francis, that no one could be afraid of it. But down below these high walls and thick gates the country runs away to the valley below; olive-trees, wheat-fields, vineyards; lands tinged with a shade of harshness as of some old, strong underrunning character of life in them, but green and gray, pointed with black cypresses; a landscape and a vista as serene as an idyl and, through that Umbrian air, as mild as images in water.

On my very first day I recognized at luncheon, sitting there at a corner table half-way on to the balcony, the man and woman I had seen in Florence together. And at a table not far away was another English woman, smaller and more animated, but unmistakably English. A stocky, dark man was with her.

Afterward I used to see the beautiful English woman and her companion in the garden together or with the two others standing on the terrace, or I met them walking along the roads; but we never spoke. The other pair I did come to know before long, and we used to sit from time to time on the terrace and talk, over coffee or peaches and wine. What the relation of these two was, whether they were married or not, I could never make out. But what I did notice was that after a while the man got to sitting more and more in his room alone; and I came to have longer talks with the lady. And she, I noticed, had got into the way of drinking a little too much, and so, when she talked, to opening her heart more freely than she might have done.

One lazy afternoon Mrs. Vivian — that was her name — came out on the terrace, where I was lounging with a new edition of Morselli's "Glauco" on my knees; and popping herself down opposite me she ordered vermouth and began to chatter.

Did I know Mrs. Abercrombie? Nor Major Neville? Not yet. Fancy that! Didn't I think her very handsome? I did, very handsome, especially her fine carriage, a movement more like an Italian woman than any lady from the British Isles, if she would pardon my saying so; for English women as a rule do not walk well.

"Mais non alors par example," Mrs. Vivian replied to that, "but not at all; I haven't been knocking over the world for nothing. Say what you like." She leaned over, "But do you really know who she is? My dear friend, that's the Mrs. Abercrombie that the English newspapers have been talking about, whose suit for divorce has just been granted; she got it. She's one of the most famous people in England, I rather fancy. Have you read it all, columns and columns?"

"I'm afraid I have not. There are so many divorces," I answered.

"So many divorces, yes. But hers is a different story. Poor dear, I think she is very plucky, I do. Shall I tell you? It's one of those cases where you'd swear fate had a grudge against a mortal. Only, look at her, when you are that beautiful — well — capacity attracts, as the Indians say."

"But I shouldn't say she looked happy, do you think?" I said.

"No, perhaps not. Something about the eyes. About that restless moving around — no, perhaps not. But I must tell you. My dear, what a story! When she was eighteen she fell violently in love with an Oxford man — I don't remember his name, but it was a good one — not of the nobility exactly but connected on all

155

sides with the nobility. You know in England
how you either are or aren't connected. Her
parents objected but she would marry him; and
why not? She loved him: ah, *te souvient-il de
notre extase ancienne? Mon cher*, do you like
French poetry? But soon after the marriage
she found that he drank; *pourquoi voulez-vous
donc qu'il m'en souvienne?* Drank very hard, and
harder and harder after a while. You know how
an Englishman can make a brute of himself.
And what a proud and difficult brute too! She
found herself left at home night after night; he
meant well enough but he was weak. His
parents, to make matters worse for her, were
very strict; they had brought him up in a house
where wine was not allowed anywhere, not even
in the servants' hall. All his father could do
was to storm and threaten to cut him off, and
his mother prayed and told May, that's Mrs.
Abercrombie, to use her influence more strongly
to reclaim her husband. A case, I should say,
of, '*parle-lui tous les jours des vertus de son père,
et quelquefois aussi parle-lui de sa mère*,' if you
like that stuffy Racine and his "Andromaque."
Perhaps May liked to enjoy herself a little, who
knows, and why shouldn't she? She was so

young and had married before she had had any
social experience at all. *Combien je regrette* —
Béranger? Am I drawing it out? Well, at any
rate, it got so bad that she saw that the only
thing to do was to separate him from his London associations. She went to Australia with
him, where the family had investments. Sheep,
I fancy, something like that, isn't Australia
sheep? Yes, of course, it's sheep, Australia,
sheep. However — At first it was better, perhaps the new life helped. At any rate, she
roughed it and in spite of her homesickness
stuck it out for two years. But by that time
he was drinking again, and she simply got up
and brought him back to England — for you
can see yourself, my dear, what was the use?
In London they went to live with his parents,
thinking that might be better. His mother
told May that she ought to stay in in the evenings
and amuse her husband and keep him out of
harm's way. Night after night May stayed in.
But her husband discovered old friends and
started drinking again. And since his family
thought it improper for her to go out alone or
with other men, May just sat there with these
two dreadful old people. Finally one night the

idea came into her head to run away. She walked out of the house and went to the Cecil, near by. There she ordered a fire in her room, cigarettes, and a bottle of champagne; and proposed to spend a happy evening once again, free. She went up to her rooms, she said, and thought she'd have a good tuck-down. But about ten o'clock the door opened and her husband's mother and father came in — and she sitting there with the champagne and cigarettes before the fire. Imagine! *Madrigal triste!* She had registered under her own name — odd, but she had — and they had had no trouble in finding her. They persuaded her to go home with them, said that she might get a divorce or anything, but let's not have a scandal. But she could not bear that life again and after a month went away quietly to an apartment of her own and started proceedings for a separation. Perhaps she had a rather gay life then, I don't know. At any rate, my dear, just then Henry Abercrombie came back from Canada and looked her up; he had heard she was in trouble. Doesn't it sound like a novelette? Wait till you hear this. At the same time her husband had a fall from his horse fox-hunting and was killed. So

she and Henry after less than a year were
married. They took an apartment together
with an old friend of Henry's who had just
married also. Life seemed happier than it had
ever been and two or three years passed like
that, Henry a devoted husband. But his health
was not good and they decided to come to the
Riviera for the winter — that was last year, you
know. And then when they were stopping at
Arles on the way down, what should the poor
thing do but break her leg, and you can't help
thinking what a fine one it is, too, to be getting
broken. That laid her up. So they wrote to
the friends in London with whom they had been
living to come and join them at Arles; it was
very dreary, you see, waiting there. So they
came down. And just before the friends came,
as luck would have it, May found a note from
Henry, a violent love-letter, written to this very
woman they had gone to live with. She taxed
her friend with it, who confessed, and the truth
came out that Henry and this woman had been
in love with each other for months. They had
struggled against it but found themselves swept
along. All that time he'd been deceiving her.
May had thought Henry the most faithful lover

imaginable, model husband. Well, she left him there and came on down to Florence. And there she found Ted Neville, who had written her already that he had retired from the army and come home from India, and would like to see her and her husband, for he had no family of his own and all that money. She joined him. So there you are, and what do you think of that?"

"She has got her divorce, you said?" I asked. "Then will they marry?"

"I don't think she will. She's had enough of it. Would you blame her? And nobody knows what relation they have between them, whether they are like sister and brother, or what. I'm sure I don't. Perhaps Ted's loved her from childhood. An Englishman can be like that, you know, faithful as long as life lasts. But that ought to seem easy. A race that can be faithful to boiled potatoes and boiled green-stuff every day for half a century ought to be able to remain faithful to a human being, don't you think?"

I caught the truth of that sally, and smiled. The lady herself laughed gaily and took another glass of vermouth and sat twisting her emerald ring round and round her finger before she began again:

"I don't believe May loves him. I'm sure she doesn't, poor thing; she's got nothing to do all day but read novels, and she's taking too much wine, I think. Do you notice it?"

I said I noticed Mrs. Abercrombie had more of a kind of flush around the eyes than she had had when I saw her in Florence, if that meant anything. That was it, my friend said, and what else was there to do out here in the hills? She went on:

"But May's good enough, she's just full of life and the devil, that's all. What do you think?"

I said there must be something in Mrs. Abercrombie that gave an opening for some of the bad fortune.

"Oh, I dare say," Mrs. Vivian replied to that, and waved her fingers as if to ask what that had to do with it.

"But what will become of her? Will she do anything for herself?"

"No, who knows that, my dear?" Mrs. Vivian answered. "My dear, Ted would marry her whether he loved her or not, he's such a good

161

fellow, poor dear. But he loves her; she's so
pathetic even if she doesn't whine and howl,
and the pathetic is irresistible, you know that.
*Que m'importe que tu sois sage? Sois belle!
Et sois triste!* — how much those silly little
Frenchmen know! But Italy is full of people
like this. And one couldn't marry them all, no
matter how tender one is. And what would
you have? It's something to have the courage
to carry things through and not stop *jusqu'au
dernier point exclusivement,* as I read once in
Rabelais, dreadful man!" She rattled on, and
I could see that she was seeing herself now in the
light of smart French comedy — life following
art again rather than art following life — and
she seemed very weak and scatter-brained and
hopeless, and yet tenacious, with her little brown
face and busy eyes. Beyond a certain point
life could not hit her.

I sat there long after twilight had closed,
thinking how many people there were indeed
like this in Italy. They float about unques-
tioned and have no part in the life around them.
They are fleeing from something, most of them;
from scandal at home, from family ties, or money
troubles; but mostly from themselves. Many

of them had possibilities in them once, these
people like Mrs. Abercrombie and this Ted
Neville of hers, and Mrs. Vivian; and they have
made a mess of it. They just missed being
something; but how much they are failures I
would not say until I knew how far most of us
can be called a success. They have wanted
overmuch of life, perhaps, more than their for-
tunes or their natures granted them. The ordinary human creature is willing to take the humdrum of the ordinary life; and neither asks nor
cares very long for much besides. These people
are at least better than that; they refuse to
accept the humdrum and the drab; they have
something in them that will not have it and
that drives through to some reality, however
fateful or disastrous it may be. But where
they come short is that they will not or cannot
take the humdrum and give it reality, fill it
out, endure the surface for a warmer content
that they can put into it. They have not the
patience, perhaps, for living.

People like these have enthusiasm, feeling,
courage, brilliance sometimes, and charm and
kindliness; qualities that would seem to go to
making up life and art as tube-colors to making

up a picture. But their lives are never able to
find a centre; their courage and enthusiasm and
kindliness and so on remain only colors degenerating into poorer values, the reckless or maud-
lin or sentimental; their passionate endowment
turns into mere exhaustion or luxury or ani-
mality; and their charm fades for lack of that
spiritual translucence which alone can make it
outlast youth. Only those who have the character to keep their own reality regardless of
events and places can endure such violent
wrenching from the common soil and from some
kind of social system that might serve to prop
them up.

Nearly all of these people love beauty of some
sort; and because they love beauty they are
pitiful, even though they have not the strength
to desire it or pursue it as far as greater souls
can do. And who minds them, after all; and
why need we resent their vagaries and their
moods, their little self-defense of arrogances,
their loose and uncertain ways of life? They
are only like gifted children that do not grow up;
they have souls that are a little more than the
common but will never mature. They carry
their idleness about Italy, living sometimes in

luxury and sometimes very hard; and they take their fill of beauty feverishly out of personal relationships when they have any, and lazily out of Italy herself, her light, her gardens and seas, and those towns of hers, Ravenna, Perugia, Cortona, and the rest, that are like as many poems in their quality and difference. "The orphans of the heart must turn to thee," Byron, the greatest of them all, wrote in Italy once; Italy feeds them and gives their loose and pitiful natures something that holds them to her, roaming here and there as they do, never really at home, like poor, vague stars wandering toward the rim of heaven.

On the first of May I was leaving for Florence again. Night had fallen when I sent my luggage ahead and set off down the winding hillside road to the station below. Along the way the olive orchards covered the slopes; a blue air was under the misty trees and on the ground there was a faint, hovering light. I remember thinking as I walked along that there was a kind of mystical necessity, like the urgency of dreams, for a figure moving among these shadowy trees, in this misty light and quiet land. And then suddenly at a turn of the road I saw some one coming down

165

the slope; a white shape whose progress seemed to be ineffably recorded by the dark trunks that it passed, and whose dim whiteness seemed to gather round it the whiteness of the air. It came closer and was the figure of a woman, walking alone; she was moving quietly, with one hand held slightly out.

Presently I saw, sitting on the low wall that marked the farm off from the road, a man, and recognized the Englishman. I stopped short, for I hated to intrude. And then while I stood there wondering if there might be some path that I might take, one of the little short-cuts through the fields, I heard him call to her; and then her low, warm voice:

"What is it, Ted?"

"Nothing. I thought you might like it here, you know." He made a short gesture with his stick in the direction of the hills.

"Yes," I heard her say then; "look at the light there. And the valley. How quiet it is! Give me a cigarette, old dear."

He lighted her cigarette for her and they sat there a moment before he spoke:

"I must say it's rather jolly here, you know."

XI

CRITICAL ARCHITECTURE

Mr. Edwards had been over for several months and I had seen him in the pension at Siena. He was a man moderately tall, brown-haired, and with faded blue eyes that were a little screwed up with an old, mother-taught intention of not being taken in. There was a sense of power about him, not so much about him exactly as about his forefathers; compared to some image one got through him of them, he seemed weaker and generally less than his forefathers, an impression of a strong mass shrunken, a kind of Christian ram that had dwindled and shrunk and got pointed up here and there. And his mouth twitched downward at the corners.

He was here in Italy, he had told me, because the doctor had prescribed the change for him. A nervous condition generally he had, which the war had greatly aggravated. Mr. Edwards had taken the war very seriously, had swallowed

all the newspaper propaganda as sacred and
fiery truth, and had raged from the outset to go
to the aid of the Mother Country, as he called
England. Since the war Mr. Edwards had not
seemed able to pull himself together. He had
worried too much, besides, over the atrocities
and he had knitted socks too much in the evenings, he said, to recover at once.

Mrs. Edwards had not come over with her
husband. She had launched some civic work at
home in Durham which she expected to benefit
the whole of western Massachusetts and she had
felt that she ought to stay and see it through.
And so it had been hard for Mr. Edwards at
first alone in a foreign country. But he had
got to liking Italy; and when I had seen him
last in Florence he was buying with great
abandonment at Mr. Coles's in the Borgo San
Iacopo prints, of terrible works it must be said,
Carlo Dolci, Guido Reni, Sassoferato's Madonna
with the blue veil, and educational pieces, mostly
Roman ruins, for his son, who was a professor
in a theological seminary somewhere in the
State. I had come, then, to think of Mr.
Edwards in Florence among the more second-
rate glories there, looking up historical spots

like Savonarola's cell and the tomb of Amerigo Vespucci.

So that I was surprised one day in Venice to find him in the Piazza San Marco at one of the tables of a little café that had been thrown out over the quay for the season.

It was autumn, the season in Venice when the moist wind is touched with the perfumes of that delicious death everywhere in the gardens of the town. At night the moon and the stars shone; and all day the light flooded the palaces by the canals, which were golden and rose and blue and white above their floating images. Over the bright walls dead leaves drifted down on to the paving-stones of the streets and floated on the water. The church-bells, coming in crowds at their due hours, fell on the sharp clearness of the air like great brazen flowers shaken down. And now as I sat there, I could hear music somewhere, a girl singing, poignant, almost shrill, like some secret entreaty to all the sails going out smaller and smaller on the rim of the sea. The sky was golden, fading into dusk above the golden darkening water. But in this golden twilight Venice seemed more rose-tinct and aureate than ever, more magnificently

169

proud, more gorgeous in her dream. Everything had something in it that lifted the city and its life into a kind of deeper truth, like that of art. The substance of it seemed to tremble and dilate itself.

It was the contrast of this with Mr. Edwards that had started Venice afresh in my mind. When I came back to the thought of him he looked more drab and more Durham than ever in this gorgeous world, far more so than in Siena or Florence, which have, after all, their crabbed spots and their narrow pinch of Puritanism. Certainly Mr. Edwards seemed, as Shylock said, in another connection, "no, not for Venice."

"Do you know," he said immediately after my opening salutations and inquiries, "I've come here every evening I've been in Venice to look at this Library of St. Mark's?"

"Really?" I said, not quite understanding.

"It seems to me very good."

I looked at Sansovino's façade, which I had known so long, those columns and pilasters and the panels above and that sculptured frieze; the elegant arrangement, the superb sophistication of it. How cold the mind was there! And how much knowledge, how much of the spiritual

170

indifference and magnificent mentality of the Renaissance! The golden lights fell across the façade now at this hour; the figures came more alive than their creator meant them to be. And some of their suave and fertile invention ran fast away from its rich restraint toward a sheer ecstasy in that enchanting light.

But these reflections could not help me with Mr. Edwards.

"The façade, you see," he said.

"Yes," I said.

"I find it very interesting."

"And of course," I said, "in this light, just after sunset."

"It seems to me very unusual." He stood a long time looking at Sansovino's façade. "Excellent! I presume there is a good photograph of it. I must see about that."

"Photographs are unsatisfactory, of course," I said luminously; "the reduced scale and no color and all that."

"I can get a colored one perhaps. I want you should go with me," he said, "if it is not too inconvenient."

I agreed.

My *casate* came, and he was finishing his.

We sat eating for a while in silence, both of us looking now and again at the Library of St. Mark's, which in the blue dark air had become like some great figured ivory stirring with the rhythms of its profound surface. Now and then I saw the gondoliers going down to their craft; and a seller of flowers with pyramids of jasmine passed us, and of oleanders, dull rose in the growing dusk, their perfume spreading on the languid sea air.

"I want to see my home again and my family, of course," Mr. Edwards said at length, "my wife and son and his wife — he's been married a year to-morrow. But I am sorry to leave all this. One gets accustomed to it, I guess."

"One develops new æsthetic needs," I replied absently.

But Mr. Edwards was now going to talk. "And yet, after all, it will be good to be at home," he began; "after all, it is where one belongs. And Durham of course is an exceptional place, though I am a citizen who say it. You've been there? Yes, I remember now you said you had. An exceptional place, excellent streets, splendid shade-trees, elms, unusually good educational advantages and churches and a good business

172

town." I nodded, and he went on: "And splendid old houses. Do you know the James Brown house, 1783? The Brewer house, that was 1745?" — and so on.

I did not remember them, though I privately remembered that they were about as different from one another as a set of chairs. They were simple, Mr. Edwards continued, very simple, of course, but full of a fine restraint and taste. Those phrases I recalled myself from Durham. He was going by on his way up, he said, to see his son and his daughter-in-law, a fine young woman, very unusual for these days. The daughter of a professor in Brown University. A splendid, ideal young woman. She could read Greek, could sew, and could cook, and she had written a pageant. He thought his son very fortunate. Then Mr. Edwards suddenly stopped and pulled himself together. "That reminds me," he cried — at least he almost cried, "if I'm going to-morrow I'd better go see about that photograph now while I think of it. You have your coffee on hand — no, don't trouble. I'll come back." He hurried away.

The light had died like a passion that changes little by little into a memory. And now, with the darkness falling, the lamps of the piazza had come on. And now the façade of the Library of St. Mark's was like a great painting in grisaille, incomparably complete in itself, and magical with a kind of intellectual rhythm strangely apparent in the dull glare of the lights; quietly ornate, and broadly sure of itself; and sure of those forms in it that arrested and held in marble the fleeting glory of thought.

But I was more absorbed with my problem. Romantic Venice, I could have seen that; the gondolas, the water, the serenades, the color of the Doge's Palace, the ices, Byron, Browning, the Murano glass, the trite perfume of honeymoons, the legends, and the rest. Or I could have understood some pious or mystical structure, some emotion of the soul built up in stone and full of prayers and half-lights. But not the Library of St. Mark's. What Mr. Edwards found there for himself puzzled me beyond measure.

I tried to go over in my mind this Mr. Edwards from Durham. His pinched face was full of character, a sort of tart aspic of character, it was true, but character all the same, the force to keep himself in a continuous unit of thought and will. I thought of his Durham, its homely tone, the sense in it of a green-shaded calm in a teacup; of those college girls on the streets with their athletic random, their slang, and their unlovely voices; of those ladies going by in closed automobiles, so many of them settled there on the easy cushions with tightened lips and a grim determination on their faces, but toward what, I could never make out; the determination to be determined, I suppose. I thought of those fine and tingling winter days, all whiteness, full of energy and drive; and of their dull evenings, propped up with the middle-class Anglo-Saxon's reverence for mere dulness, or by the citizens flattering themselves that all this was a deep life of thought. I recalled most of the culture in Durham, a passable taste in safe, stale things. I thought of Durham's pious political eloquence, slightly catarrhal; of its churchgoers and its sly gay dogs. And of the handful of people of living and beautiful worth, torturing themselves into staleness for lack of enough to whet their lives upon in such an atmosphere. And I thought of those houses, Browns, Brewers, and the rest, that Mr. Edwards had remembered phrases to praise.

175

They did have a certain simplicity, charm, or even elegance in a small way. The poetry, too, they had of old tea-caddies and candlesticks and parental affection, however quiet, of long-dead faces and half-forgotten hymnologies. But what a pity that so much attention as they got from Durham inhabitants and visitors could not be also applied to an art more ample, august, and significant, and capable of wider experience!

What I pondered was this: If Mr. Edwards was so impressed with Sansovino's façade, what effect did it have on him? In the first place, how could he so easily like Durham architecture and Sansovino's, of which in style Durham's best was a distant descendant? But that much was not so difficult. The two things satisfied two wants of his nature. Or they were compensations for repressions that had gone on, inhibitions. And perhaps his mind was compartmental, watertight compartments — to use the phrase attributed to a hundred people. Very well. But my problem remained, nevertheless. It was this:

How can you really see the point of Sansovino's art, and that art not be a criticism on

176

yourself, on the rest of your living and thinking, on your taste, which after all emerges from the kind of man you are? It ought not to make you dislike Durham, but it ought certainly to make you see how lean a phrase Durham is in life and in art. The problem of Mr. Edwards brought to mind professors I have known who spoke of being in a state they described as reading through an author, Sophocles for example. But what exactly, I always wondered, do they get from it of any depth if the Sophoclean does not become a comment and criticism of their minds and souls, a pulse in their lives and a quality of their days? If Mr. Edwards really saw Sansovino's art, there ought to be something in its formal elegance, warm rhythm and dignity and copious invention that would make him demand some august and fertile distinction in his own life and thinking and relationships. And that would make him want a number of added qualities in his daughter-in-law before she became Ideal Woman. And if Mr. Edwards really sees the point in Sansovino, the famed sincerity of the Brown house ought to shrink no little by the unavoidable comparison with Sansovino's work, with that rich, fluent,

177

and elaborate material here unified into a large simplicity by fine artistic domination. At least Mr. Edwards would have to take a stand one way or the other on these two estates and credos of living. It is quite all right to love Durham, but not to talk nonsense about it. Or must one be an artist to make this large transcription of an art into one's own condition?

I thought of the arid cramp of those speeches of Mr. Edwards' in praise of the Library of St. Mark's: the façade, you see, it seemed to him very good, he found it unusual; and then of the monologue about Durham and its virtues. The image of that face rose again in my mind; something about it of a wistful, converted snapping-turtle. It looked more pinched than ever in the midst of all this accomplishment, this release, this abundance of living, these *invenzioni*, *mirabilissime e infinite cose*, these inventions, most marvellous and infinite things, that Leonardo used to tell his pupils of; this goodness and delight that spread from a profound art into the body and mind. By contrast with all this how pitiful seemed the record written on that intent face, the record on Mr. Edwards' face of foolish inhibitions exercised often with no intelligent end or foresight, but only for their own sake; the stamp there of egotistical indulgence in remorse and conscience and meaningless negation, sustained by complacent and jealous provincialism. Egotistical indulgence, remorse, conscience, self-complacency! I wondered what Sansovino and Venice had done to the states of mind and being in Mr. Edwards. If Mr. Edwards found himself the same and his satisfactions with Durham the same after all this, how much did he see at all what Sansovino meant?

He came back.

"The man had none in stock," he stated, "or so he said. I had to order a photograph sent to me. I suppose he is reliable."

"Quite," I said, automatically.

"Well, then, I must say good-by and get back to my hotel and have my dinner and pack up. I leave early in the morning." We shook hands. I wished him a pleasant journey.

"If you should come to Durham again, let me know," he said; and turned away. I saw him stop a little way off and look around him once, slowly; then he disappeared down the arcade.

The late moon had come up now and the piazza lamps had been cut off save for a few here and there. Venice had grown quieter, for the evening gaieties were not yet arrived. From my far corner of the great square the noises of the city seemed far away. The dip of an oar measured the silence. The hour seemed to be made up of the silence that preceded a sound and the silence that followed it. But the measure of the oar was like a living pulse, there was nothing sterile or mechanical in it. And the rhythm of it everywhere, I knew, would be moving in the sleeping water the reflections of the stars. The moonlight now was creeping across the wide piazza, strangely white; it touched the firm elegance and definity of the marble columns where they rose from the silver pavement. I watched the light climb higher and higher and rest at length on the frieze, whose figures sprang with that into life again, and whose elegance settled again upon it. The mind, I thought, has its passionate distinction, and the magnificent chaos of emotion in us has, nevertheless, its deep urgency of order and pattern and its cold unity underneath. And in great art like this I could see the gorgeous and august necessity in life;

180

and the heroic need in a large nature for moral domination of its powers.

I realized, as I sat there thinking, that Durham was fast becoming for me a problem in æsthetics. But it was human, too, and humanly it seemed far away and most unfruitful, and yet not without its poignant hidden beauty and pathos and heart. But like, too, a tune played on a little organ by a villager, stern and thin and insistent and quavering, with one stop always out and heard by hosts of Edwardses, who like it well enough and speak of it a little stubbornly as fine and simple. And how much, I asked myself, could Mr. Edwards read of this design by which an artist has written at least one comment on Durham's meagre ways of life? And how far was Mr. Edwards Durham-blind to the elaborate and abundant art of the Library of St. Mark's; in which the silent music of the motionless lines was so powerful that it created an illusion of a life richer and more beautiful than this life we have? Not of the highest reach of the soul, not that, but yet the music of intellectual beauty remaining true even now beneath the pressure of the moon's poetry and the Venetian night.

XII

COUNTRY GODS

The *festa* of San Pancrazio lasted through two days because of the saint's hospitality. St. Peter was his guest for the festival; coming from his own home down the hill where the road turns off into the country, just as San Pancrazio himself had come from his home under the mountain looking down over the water. The crowd for the parade on the second night was innumerable, for the whole town was out and all the countryside for miles. The Taormina band was present by order of the Sindaco, in three-cornered hats and feathers; and the Syracuse band with cockades had come. San Pancrazio and San Pietro had to travel from the Church of the Virgin, far down at the west end of the town, to make a visit to the Duomo; though, like the sly pieties they were, they had really been there up to that moment already, the whole two days in fact, getting presents and offerings and having their pictures sold. From the Virgin's church they were to go the entire length

182

of the Corso to their homes outside the walls.
Every one made his best showing that night,
the gentlemen in their Palermo tailoring, the
ladies with all their jewels on; the workmen in
brighter jackets and sashes; the contadini, some
of the men in old knee-breeches or boots and
caps three centuries back in style, and the women
in shawls with long earrings reaching to their
shoulders and full skirts like hoops.

Booths and barrows lined the streets, selling
fireworks and drinks, knives and ribbons and
torrone made of new almonds and honey; and
alternating with the merchandise and drinks were
the gambling-stands. There were a dozen rou-
lette-tables, silver horses whirling around over
the numbered courses where you put your *soldo,*
and bright arrows with painted feathers that
stopped whirling sooner or later and left a light
tip resting on the lucky number. Crowds of
people were putting their money down, mostly
little boys, it seemed, who bent forward over
their money and shrieked and swore. The
rockets were firing from every direction, brilliant,
scattering far up overhead, with reports like
bombs, unbelievably loud, to appease the Sicilian
liking for mere noise. Now and then firecrack-

ers in bunches were thrown from the roofs of
the churches into the little stone streets, with
a rattling and detonation like a bombardment.
Beside the Duomo the band from Syracuse was
playing airs from the opera. Meantime the deep
blue of the early night had fallen over the walls,
and over that country dropping down toward
the sea and rising on the other hand toward
the Saracen castle above the town. A few pale
stars were out and a slender moon, almost past,
was shining. The whole piazza was sweet with
the perfume of the jessamine that ran along the
front of the house next the church, incredible
sweetness in that soft, blue air. And everywhere were the voices, deep and bright.

Presently the other band was heard coming
nearer; the Syracusan made a final flourish and
left off. Lights appeared through the archway
beneath the clock; then, more distinctly, a gold-
en canopy and lamps burning about a figure,
gilded and painted all over, with a high, jewelled
crown on his head. The round dome was like
that of an Indian rajah set on twisted columns,
rococo with heavy grapes that twined over
them. Under it St. Peter sat. He was covered
with rings and watches and chains that blazed

in the light of his flaring and somewhat gaudy lamps. After him, and carried also on twenty or thirty shoulders, came San Pancrazio himself in a finer and larger tabernacle, rectangular, with more lamps and more brocade and jewelry and presents. He appeared to be completely entangled in chains, coral drops, bracelets, rings, and pins, and strings of five-lire notes that hung down from his wrists. The patron saint of the town San Pancrazio was; and though he had to be painted black because he had come first from Africa, you see, signore, fifteen centuries ago, and was very ugly with that great staring head and thick mouth, what blessings he had shown Taormina and favors in Paradise! Indeed, signore, who does not know the time he saved the town from fever, when the sacristan saw his eyes move, up of course, where heaven is?

With the saint came the nuns, carrying long tapers and Our Lady's banner, sky-blue and bound with wreaths of flowers. And the little communicants with their white gauze veils and their white bouquets and white candles followed after, great-eyed little girls with their crackling white, exactly like icing figures from a cake. They, too, had banners; and the priests, the stu-

dents, every one, had standards and streamers
and banners, red, orange, blue, white, with gold
and silver fringes flashing in the light of the
candles, the tapers, the torches, the flaring
acetylene lanterns on those green arches across
the street. Every one was laughing and talking.
The little boys at the roulette-wheels laughed
and cursed and banged their money down; and
the Syracuse band set up again with a medley
from "Carmen," all under this night of jasmine
perfume and blue air.

Later we saw the saint's home-coming, after
he had made a visit in St. Peter's church. They
set him in his shrine in the dark, bare little
church with all his lamps about him. The
church roared with laughter and shouts: "Ad-
dio, Santo!" "Good-by!" "Remember us!"
"Don't forget Taormina!" People ran up and
played a sort of tag with the saint, touching his
robe and jumping away; and cracked jokes and
whistled at him. And he meanwhile sat glitter-
ing there, looking out over their heads with his
big eyes and his black, ugly face, blessing them
with that enormous uplifted hand and doing
them a great deal of good, as everybody knew.
And then the lamps were put out, with every one

departing, and the door closed, and only the little devoted tapers were left to burn that night at his feet till they were ended.

Later, on my balcony that night, I thought of the religion of all this and of some of my friends at home and what they would think of it. A pretty piece of paganism, as Wordsworth said of Keats's poem; they would think that, no doubt. For religion with them, if I should ask them what it was, would be an inner thing, some conception of God that came from one's inner consciousness, something worshipped in prayer and silence, after long, deep, serious thinking. But while they told me that, I should be wondering if length of time and seriousness have much to do with the power to think or the importance of thought, though it might comfort these un-Sicilian friends of mine to believe so. Shall we not even allow Taormina the procession? I might inquire. Well, then, at least not such a hubbub, they might answer, at least not the bull-fighter's song for a religious occasion. And not the gambling! And not so much worship of saints, and even of saints' bones! And yet, I should be thinking, how plain it must be that people's religion is not ready-made; whatever they are,

187

their religion must be, big or little, bright or dark, dim or open, inner or objective. My friends, however, would never admit that, otherwise what of the true religion, the one and only —— ?

But if my friends were going to send Plymouth Rock and Georgia and Ohio to church on the east coast of Sicily — if they were to breathe the pews upon this race made up of Greek and Roman and Saracen, Spanish and African blood, dwelling in the open reality of this bright sun, this changing verdure and drouth and rocks, this shadow of Etna over all to establish life and death as certainties beyond any possible illusion — what argument might I make?

And then suddenly came a crash of bells, brazen, barbaric, happy. I heard them and remembered how many things are in heaven and earth. The contest that had reared itself in my mind was after all with the regulation Protestant standpoint, which removes the ground of all things to the mind, whether one has a mind or not, to set up bounds and altars there. Taormina might well let my friends be, with this God of theirs behind the clouds or behind the stove or wherever that inner eye might see him; and my friends might let Taormina be. There could be no argument. I heard the throaty, bright roar of the bells, and marked how different they were from the bells in England and Georgia and Boston, which were sweeter and more pealing and sentimental.

I thought of these people in the streets, what they were. Their voices flared up and down, they laughed, burst into song, were grave again; they met and kissed each other, they talked gravely, they made scufflings and fisti-cuffs; these sudden shocks of life and vividness struck and seemed to pass through them. The forces of life seemed to move through them as the wind moves through trees. Even their faces and their bodies had a distinctness as if shaped by the struggle of growing forces; as the trees and plant forms are distinct about them, shaped by the struggling of water and wind and sun and the earth. I recalled a little girl that I had seen. Her body was straight, and she walked smoothly as a cat; her shock of sun-burnt, harsh hair, her smooth, dark skin and black, tragic, wild eyes belonged to the land, the rocks, the dust, the sun; her little feet seemed to grow out of the earth. And all

189

around her were faces, characters, with the life of
the earth written on them. How easy it is here,
on the coast of Sicily and among these people,
to understand the way in which the Mediterranean art, literature, sculpture, and dramatic
masks ran so constantly to general symbols,
and to types, to the larger simplicities of nature,
within which her subtleties are written! Not
that there seems really more of life and nature
here than in the North; but that it seems more
distinct. We get the sense of life carrying these
beings along and then later wearing them out,
consuming them with what they had been nourished by.

Nature seems to be tested here. Here we can
judge whether we like nature or not. This
seems to be about what nature intended; and
only afterward arose all those complicated or-
ganisms that we call civilized. I feel that here
I can see things in a matrix of nature. And
this accounts for the impression I get of passion in these people, but of little sentiment.
I get the impression of brutality sometimes, of
a violent animalism, but never of vulgarity;
vulgarity is more confused and more involved
with society than with a deeper natural current.

These people seem not hard so much as natural.
Their step when they walk is as free as a horse's;
they have clear, able minds, unfuddled with
cant and introspection. They cry and laugh,
but they do not brood very much. Their fingers are apt and quick; they are generous with
gifts, and make hard bargains; they have pity
in their hearts but not so much in their souls;
their pity is quick, human, but not long and
troubled and profound. Their tragedy is hard
and clear and violent, fatal but not depressing.
They accept fate, they shrug their shoulders;
one does as one must. What would you have?
What does the proverb say? Necessity makes
the old woman run. They must have noises
about them to equal the brightness of the light.
They can sleep, like birds and animals, through
any noise, songs, drums, carts on stone, donkeys,
and church-bells; and anywhere, in a doorway,
by a wall, under a roadside tree.

And I think of these people as tied to the earth
by the bread they eat. That old figure of
speech, the staff of life, here goes back to its
first reality; for a piece of bread is enough and
often is all they have. I see bread, bread;
children stand in doorways eating bread; and

191

old men sit down at a wine-table or by a wall and take out a piece of bread to eat. The poetry of bread is theirs, Ceres, Demeter, the mother Earth. They are the Earth's children and lean on her breast. What other kind of gods and saints and festivals could they have? What gods but bright gods and human gods, able to make bargains; gods who are social? For if one wishes to give San Pancrazio a watch or a five-lire note and rings and gold chains, the saint himself must be obliging; he must show us favors and come to his *festa* when there are parades and rockets and roulette and drinks and music and candles. And if a man loves these blessed ones in Paradise, the good God and Madonna and her Son, and afterward the saints, San Pancrazio and Peter, San Giovannino and the rest — who were human themselves once, we can tell you, and now live with God, though they like to have their shrines on earth and crowns and *festas* — if one loves these rightly here in Taormina, one will be a good man. A good man is a man who, after God and the saints, loves his family and is happy with them; who likes to see other people and laugh and talk with them, even if he gets angry sometimes — though it is not so bad in this province as it is in Girgenti, where a man will kill you for a snap of the finger; who marries early, drinks a little wine, works hard, goes to mass, pays his dues, and finally grows old with fine sons and daughters and plenty of grandchildren to come to see him in the donkey-carts, with old Maria or Annunziata, his wife, sitting outside by the door with him, two white heads, not many teeth any more; and now and then a visit from the padre, to whom it is best to leave a little something in the will; and finally a proper burial. That was a good man, people will say of you then.

I looked at the night about me. There had been an early moon setting in the west and now there was only starlight. It was long past twelve, past one; but I could see an old man and all his family sitting out in front of their house talking gaily together, and the carts were just beginning to go home. The carts came by one after another, rattling on the stones of the road. In every one they sang; strange, bright voices echoing along the rocks and down the walled roads. One after another I heard these songs, none of them more than three lines, sung over and over again, sometimes in two voices, sometimes a sort of counter-singing of four, and often a whole chorus, those in the cart and those